298

young animals

Maurice Burton

young animals

Hamlyn

Published by
the Hamlyn Publishing Group Limited
London, New York, Sydney, Toronto
Hamlyn House, Feltham, Middlesex, England
first published 1965
second edition 1970
SBN 600395014

printed in Czechoslovakia by Polygrafia, Prague

contents

domestic animal babies 6

rearing wild animals in captivity 24

learning and instinct 37

at play 59

danger 72

growing up in the wild 90

foster-parents 108

riding pick-a-back 117

babies in pouches 136

oddities and ends 143

acknowledgments 152

Several years ago our Sheltie had puppies. 'Sheltie' is short for Shetland sheep dog, and like the famous Shetland pony the Sheltie is a small breed.

As the time drew near for the puppies to be born the Sheltie began to be restless. She had had several litters of puppies before, and it is possible she may have remembered something about what happened then. But she would not have known, as a human mother knows, what was about to take place. The reason for her restlessness was that something was stirring within her body. Not only were the puppies themselves stirring, but all manner of other events were taking place within her.

While the puppies are developing within the womb they are being nourished from the mother's blood, and the waste from the bodies of the puppies is passed back into her body to be eliminated. So there is a constant exchange between mother and unborn puppies. In addition, many chemical changes are taking place during this time. Chemical messengers are given out from various glands, which pass into the mother's blood and are carried around her body. They are messengers in the sense that they start from one place but cause a change to take place in another. The changes they set up are all in preparation for the great day when the puppies are born and leave the sheltered world within the mother's body for a more active life on their own.

Some examples of these changes are seen in the way the teats grow larger; the milk glands just inside the body at the bases of the teats begin to produce milk; other chemical messengers affect the behaviour of the mother animal. A few days before their babies are due to be born many mother animals strip the hair from their front, with the result that the teats are more fully uncovered. Not all animal mothers do this. Some of the best examples are seen in rabbits and foxes, which not only expose the teats but use the fur they strip from their bodies for making a nest.

If we are to understand baby animals and the things they do, it is important to remember that neither they nor their parents can think things out. It is possible that some of the higher animals are capable of a certain amount of real thought, but at best it is limited. Certainly, they have no books in which to find out what must be done when their babies are born. They have no doctors, nurses, clinics or hospitals. And when the youngsters themselves are growing up there are no teachers or schools where they can be educated. This means that they must go through life guided largely by instinct.

This is a word which includes many different forms of behaviour, and while it is not possible to go into great detail here we shall indicate some of the actions which we call instinctive. And all the time we need to remember that instinctive

Fauntleroy and his sister Poppet, the Sheltie pups at five weeks old. The personalities of these two pups are already apparent even at this age: Poppet on the left being much livelier, more agile and sharper than her brother

Fauntleroy and his mother Suki

With mother keeping watch a family of Basset hounds, seven weeks old, lines up for lunch

actions start within the body or the brain. Some of them are called forth by the chemical messengers already mentioned, others are called forth by what the animal experiences through its senses.

Whatever may have been the cause of the Sheltie's restlessness, the result was that she wandered about and finally settled on a place where the puppies should be born. As it happened, she chose a rug in an outhouse. There, late in the evening, the birth took place; two of the puppies were stillborn and two are alive today.

When first born the puppies were not pretty. Their bodies were covered with only a thin layer of very short hair. Their eyes were sealed tight and so were their ears. At first they lay with very little movement, their bodies wet with the birth fluids. Instinctively, the mother began to lick each one, until all the fluid had been removed. By now, the two live puppies were beginning to move their legs feebly. They also started to wriggle their bodies, and to move their heads around as if they were searching for something. They had been born with an overwhelming hunger and a sense of smell, and little more besides. This was, however, all that was necessary at this stage. It gave them the urge to search for the mother's teats, and their sense of smell guided them to the teats.

For several days, the two puppies did little more than sleep and feed. While asleep they nestled close to each other and to the mother. When awake they jostled each other feebly as they searched for the mother's teats. All the mother had to do was to keep them warm, let them feed and keep them clean. Then, on the twelfth day, their eyes opened. By that time, also, they were able to make more use of their legs. Their muscles were becoming stronger and they were moving about more. Even so, it was a week or more after this before they began to stray much from the place where they were born.

It is a very different story for the foal, or baby horse. In fact, it is because this

youngster so soon learns to stand on its own feet that we seldom speak of 'baby' horse but use the word 'foal'. Usually there is only one foal born to a mare, rarely are there twins. It is born with the eyes open, with a good coat of hair, and with legs long in proportion to the body. Very soon after it is born the foal tries to get on to its feet. Its first attempts are shaky and feeble, but at last it rises on to its four legs. Then, for the next few minutes, we see it wobbling, almost falling at each step, even falling completely at times. As we watch it we see that it has not yet gained complete control of its limbs and seems on the point of falling, first to one side, then to the other, almost every second. There is one thing that catches the eye: although the limbs are wobbly, the foal is saved again and again by its sense of balance. We see it almost fall and then in the nick of time move its weight so as to correct its balance. So it goes on, improving both in the use of the legs and in its sense of balance, until about an hour after the time of birth the foal is able to walk or even run, and within a few hours it is able to keep up with its mother.

The period of time between conception and birth is known as the gestation period. In the domestic dog this period lasts only 60 to 65 days. In the horse it is from 330 to 340 days. While it is true that in small animals the gestation

period is shorter than in larger animals of the same kind, the difference is not so great as between 60 and 330 days. What this means is that the puppy is born at a less advanced stage than the foal. Several interesting points arise from this.

To begin with, a bitch has to carry her puppies for a much shorter period, and to this extent she has the lesser burden. Consequently we find that while horses and other hoofed animals have, as a rule, one offspring at a birth, the bitch may have a litter of up to five or more puppies, usually from three to five. Another effect is that she is tied to one place until the puppies are able to run freely and strongly, whereas the mare can move about over wide distances within a few hours of having dropped her foal.

These differences are related to the feeding habits of the two kinds of animals. The dog is a hunter and a flesh-eater. In a wild state a bitch would leave her puppies for a while to go hunting, or she would be supplied by her mate. In either event the practical result is that it is possible to bring the food to one spot which, so long as the puppies are helpless or unable to run strongly, constitutes 'home'. Wild horses live in herds which crop the grass and must be continually on the move. They must be able to move from one pasture to another. They must also be able to take flight if attacked by a flesh-eater, and the need for escape from an enemy may occur soon after the foal is born.

So we have a general rule that the flesh-eaters bear young that are helpless at birth and are born after a short gestation, are more numerous and are nursed in one spot. Grass-eaters give birth to one young as a rule, and the single baby is able to run within a short time of being born, and must be able to move about with the herd at an early age.

There are exceptions to all rules and this is no less true of baby animals than of anything else. The young deer is born in much the same way as the foal, and as with the baby horse this may be the reason that it seems wrong to speak of a baby deer, because it looks and behaves so like its parents almost from the moment of birth, apart from the fact that it is unable to find its own food. It is usual to speak of the young of the larger deer, such as the red deer or wapiti, as a calf; of the young of medium-sized deer as fawns; and of the young of the smaller deer, such as the roe, as a kid.

The fawn or kid is dropped in a spot where there is thick undergrowth. We notice that, although the coat of the mother red deer or the mother roe deer is a more or less uniform colour, the coat of the fawn or the kid is spotted, and there may be a reason for this: the spots break up the outline of the body, and a fawn or kid lying among tall vegetation is not easy to see; it is certainly true that when the sun is shining through the bushes, dappling the undergrowth with light and shadows, the dappled fawn is concealed against the background.

Even the adult deer lying in the same situation is very difficult to see, in spite of having no spots on the coat. By contrast, both the adult deer and the spotted fawn can be seen the moment they move. What makes the fawn so difficult to find is the fact that during the early days of its infancy it instinctively 'freezes' at the first sign of danger. It remains crouched and lowers its head and neck to the ground, and in this position keeps perfectly still. It does this only so long as there is the likelihood of an intruder not coming too close. Try to pick up the fawn and it will jump to its feet and leap and bound in a most agile and erratic manner, so that it is very difficult to catch.

Left: a young Shetland pony grazing; its legs are disproportionately long; it must bend the front legs to reach the ground with its muzzle

A young donkey

A black-faced lamb samples his milk before feeding time

People do find fawns or kids, and some, quite mistakenly, pick them up: mistakenly, because they think the fawn has been abandoned, whereas if they knew the truth the mother is grazing near by. What happens with deer is that the fawn is dropped in dense cover and the mother later goes off to feed. She does not go far away and every so often she returns to suckle her baby.

The fawn's habit of freezing and then of taking agile evasive action if necessary is instinctive. Every fawn does it, and does it in the same way. That is how we know it is not learned, but is a behaviour pattern with which the fawn is born. It is an inherited pattern which comes out at the appropriate moment, or, as we say, it is instinctive. When people find fawns and pick them up, it means that the fawn is not very old and that the instinct to freeze is already there but the instinct to take evasive action has not been fully developed. Instinctive actions come out at the appropriate moment, just as the chemical messengers in the mother's body, before the baby is born, come into play at the right time. Indeed, if there were not this well-ordered time-table very

Under domestication the mother animal is apt to have larger families than in the wild, bringing obvious disadvantages to her

few animals would ever be born, and of those that were very few would ever survive. Things would always be going awry.

There is another side to this difference between the baby flesh-eaters like the dog and the cat, and the grass-eaters or vegetable-eaters like the horse, deer, cow and sheep. The young hoofed animal must be able to keep itself warm and must be able to stand up to the rigours of the weather. There is no coddling for them, and they do not need it. The bitch not only leaves her puppies in a warm nest—usually this is a blanket or other warm material supplied by her owner—but she can lie down with her puppies and let them nestle into her body for warmth. Foals, fawns, calves and lambs not only have no warm nest but they have some difficulty in nestling into the mother's body. So we find lambs being born successfully in the snow, calves being born in the open field, and some of the most successful pig-breeders are those that give the piglets no more shelter than a few trusses of straw to shelter them from the cold winds.

In one sense the birth and growth of a baby animal is almost machine-like. In a manufactured article one part must be made first, then another, and the two fitted together; and in this mechanical age, in which raw materials are fed into a complicated machine from which the completed article comes out at the other end, as one stage in manufacture is completed the machinery for the next is automatically set into motion for the next stage. The baby developing inside the mother's body, and the infant developing its instincts and strengthening its muscles, proceeds in much the same fashion. There is, however, one very big difference. A batch of articles produced by machine all look and behave very much alike. In the living baby there is developed, in due course, what is known as a personality.

The Sheltie's two puppies showed this very well. One of them was a male. As he grew in size his coat became a glistening reddish colour, but he had a collar of white hair which reminded us of the lace collar worn by little Lord Fauntleroy. So he was named Fauntleroy, or Fauntle for short. Fauntle is a most adorable dog, but beside his sister he seemed slow and dull-witted and this was evident from the first days that they began to move about. Later, when they were able to run about and play together, she was always the faster,

A New Forest mare and her foal grazing. The foal is nibbling the grass but not really eating it

Keeping the family together can be a problem for this ewe

14

more agile, more spirited and more mischievous. In fact, it seemed perfectly natural to use the present-day idiom and say 'she is a poppet'. And that was how she was named, Poppet. Her coat is mainly black, with some white and a few reddish-brown patches. Even if the two puppies had been the same colour and size we should never have been in any doubt which was Fauntle and which was Poppet.

To give only one example of this difference in personality between the two puppies: when Fauntle came towards me to be petted he did so staidly and soberly, wagging his tail and lifting his upper lip on both sides of the face in what looked like a grin. It is a warm enough greeting but very sedate. Poppet come bounding up, not only wagging her tail but wriggling her whole body, and jumping up repeatedly, a bounding, jumping, wriggling and writhing bundle of black and white. For in any litter—whether of puppies, kittens or whatever it may be—no matter how much they may look alike, each baby animal is born with a personality, just as it is born with instincts. But whereas the pattern of the instincts does not vary appreciably from one to another, the personality varies enormously. More will be said about this when we come to deal with baby wild animals in captivity.

The two favourite pets are dogs and cats, and since so much has been said about dogs it would be unfair not to give cats the limelight for a while. In fact, much of what has been said about dogs and puppies is equally true for cats and kittens.

There is one marked difference between cats and dogs, however. Cats, as a race, are much more independent. In the wild they are solitary animals, whereas the ancestors of the domestic dog, if only we could be sure what its ancestors were, must have been in the habit of roaming in packs. Members of a pack are dependent on each other; solitary animals must be independent. So, when the she-cat feels the restlessness at the approaching birth of her

kittens, she behaves somewhat differently from the Sheltie. This is more marked in some cats than others. There are cats, for instance, which are thoroughly friendly and affectionate towards their owners, keeping close to them, allowing themselves to be petted, and acting in every way as companions—until the time is approaching when their kittens are to be born. Then it sometimes happens that the cat seems to turn against its human friends. She goes away from the house, chooses some out-of-the-way spot where she will have her kittens, and apart from coming back to the house regularly for her meals as usual, she evades everybody so that they do not find out about her kittens until she proudly leads them in when they are old enough.

Sometimes such a cat will choose an outhouse that is not very much used, or she may go farther afield and quite literally have her kittens in a field, in a nest she has prepared in a hedge or among some bushes. Should you chance upon this nest accidentally, while the mother is away, you will then see how the mother's independence comes out in the kittens. Small puppies still being suckled may be slightly shy at the approach of a stranger and may even seem to be afraid, but a nestful of kittens in a bush will, when a stranger approaches while their mother is away, open their tiny mouths, show their teeth and

Exuberant moorland pony foals 'boxing' for the fun of it

This yak calf will grow up to be a beast of burden on the Tibetan plateau

This Syrian bear cub at the
London Zoo seems fond of his
keeper

The Bactrian camel seen here
with her young has been
domesticated for thousands
of years

A proud Collie mother with
her family

The llama of South America
with her young, a beast of
burden in the High Andes

Thoughtful expressions from
two adorable puppies

hiss. It is, however, more show than anything else, because usually you can pick the kittens up and stroke them and they will not struggle, except perhaps to try to get back into the nest. Then, when you put them back, they will once again show their teeth and hiss, if you put your hand towards them—but will be quite tame if you pick them up again.

Earlier, when speaking of instinct, the impression was given that so much about the birth and growing up of baby animals has almost a machine-like pattern. Even the parent's behaviour has some such qualities: the mother automatically looks for a place to have her kittens, she automatically licks them when they are born, and so on. It was even said that the animal mother cannot know anything about the birth of her young, as a human mother does. It would be wrong to run away with the idea that the whole of his wonderful process of introducing new life to the world is automatic and soulless. Not only have we to recognise that, in the higher animals at least, there is a mother-love, but to all appearances there seems to be mother-pride.

20

Adventurous youth: a kitten's
first venture in climbing leads
to some uncertainty

An Abyssinian cat with her
kitten

During the time that the Sheltie bitch had her puppies she would look up at anyone going to see them with a mute appeal in her eyes, almost as if asking the question: 'What do you think of them?' It is, however, always easy to read far more into an animal's actions than is justified. Nevertheless, some of the stories about cats and their kittens do suggest that the mother cat is proud of her litter. Many people have told how their cat, after having disappeared to have her kittens, has brought them home when they are old enough, or has even carried them, one by one, in her mouth to set them at the feet of her owner-friend, and then looked up as if to ask: 'Aren't they wonderful?'

Cats go even further than this, and the following story is only one of many on these lines. In this instance the owner of the cat was unaware that she had kittens, although he suspected that something was afoot. One afternoon he was digging in the garden when he felt something tugging at his trouser-leg. Turning, he saw it was his cat. He bent down and stroked her, and then went on with his digging, but the cat continued to pull at his trouser-leg and to walk away. He did not follow, so the cat came back and again pulled at him. Finally, he assumed the cat was trying to tell him to follow her, which he did. She led him to an old shed, and there he saw the kittens. As he looked at them the cat stood by him, looking up at him as if to say: 'Aren't they wonderful?'

The story of animal babies contains a whole string of details about instincts, learning and glimpses of intelligent behaviour, but for the most part it is the story of how Nature, as we put it for the sake of simplicity, equips animals before and after birth and throughout their lives to look after themselves without having to think about it, but this does not mean that they are entirely without some of the gentler qualities of which we ourselves are capable.

22

The surprise is that the genet was not domesticated in place of the cat. The genet kittens are highly attractive, agile and beautifully marked, readily tamed if taken young. The Cats of Constantinople were, in fact, not pussies but tame genets

Domestic animals often form friendships with one another, like this kitten with a dog

rearing wild animals in captivity

Most of our familiar domesticated animals were domesticated so long ago that we have little idea how this was brought about. It is said that the dog was domesticated perhaps as long as 100,000 years ago. As a result, we have no real idea about its ancestors. Some scientists maintain that the dog is descended from the wolf, others that it was derived partly from the wolf and partly from the jackal, and yet others believe there may have been a wild dog which has disappeared as a wild animal.

We are hardly less in the dark about the domestic cat. We know that the ancient Egyptians venerated and mummified a domestic cat, but even with the evidence of these mummified remains there is still some doubt whether they belonged to the cat known as the bush cat of Africa, or the jungle cat of Southern Asia but also found in North-west Africa. The strange thing is that the domesticated tabby should be so like our own wild cat, yet we are assured that the latter is in no way an ancestor of the domesticated cat. In fact, the kittens of the European wild cat are said to be quite untameable, no matter how early they are taken from the mother. But the same is said of the African bush cat, and it is believed to be true of the Asiatic jungle cat. We thus have the odd situation that an animal kept as a pet the world over should have been originally domesticated from a species that is virtually untameable.

It is even more odd when we recall that, as a rule, almost any animal can be tamed if taken early enough and hand-reared. It is worth while to look into this matter a little more closely, if only to try to guess what may have happened in the case of the cat.

American scientists have shown that in any litter of wolves there will be one cub more easily tamed than another, and that there is a wide difference between the most and the least tameable. They also found that the earlier the cubs were taken from the mother the more chance there was of taming them. These are simple statements which nobody with experience in hand-rearing the young of wild animals will disagree. The young of volves have been studied by scientists, with clearly defined results.

It would seem that there can be no bar to taming the young of any wild animal, whether bush cat, jungle cat, wild cat or any other. The difficulty arises in obtaining the babies at a sufficiently early age. The grass-eaters, as we have seen, give birth to their babies above ground and in the open. They are able to move about with their parents very soon after being born, and therefore there is no difficulty in catching them early and taming them. But the flesh-eaters have altogether different habits. These either make a nest concealed in the undergrowth, like the cat, or they have their babies underground or

Hand-rearing a young brown hare with milk in an eye-dropper. Many orphan animals find their way to captivity and need to be hand-fed and nursed in place of the mother's care

in a den, like the badger, fox, wolf or bear. Furthermore, it is not only difficult to find the nest, but even more difficult to extract the babies from it. Underground nests have to be located and dug out, and in most cases the mother has to be circumvented. The mother flesh-eater will, as a rule, fight like a tiger in defence of her young.

Even when the babies have been taken from their mothers they are very difficult to rear for reasons that will emerge later. We know so little about how this kind of animal actually brings up its babies in the wild. Because their nests are hidden it is difficult to find out by keeping a day-to-day watch on them. Then again, babies of the flesh-eaters seem to be delicate, and their successful rearing very much a matter of chance. It seems that it is only after scientific research has been done on the species that success in rearing them is attained. Indeed, it is more remarkable that our early ancestors should so successfully have domesticated such typical flesh-eaters as the cat and the dog.

At birth a baby hedgehog's spines are quite soft, but by this stage they have begun to harden

Most babies look up to their mothers, but the giraffe particularly finds this necessary

25

The pricked ears and expressive eyes give this fox cub an expression of great intelligence

This is best illustrated by the hand-rearing of baby seals. There have been many instances in the past of people who have had pet seals. These people have usually been farmers whose lands go down to the sea on a part of the coast where seals come ashore to have their babies. One hears now and then of a farmer who had a pet seal that followed him about like a dog. Usually it is found that the seal adopted the man and not the other way round. We may suspect that the seal was orphaned and very hungry, that it happened to be old enough to take solid food, and that it was probably a seal which was by its own nature extremely tameable anyway. However, this is largely guessing.

We can be more definite when we consider the attempts that have been made in zoos and by scientists studying seals to hand-rear the pups. Until a few years ago this was considered one of the most troublesome tasks. In fact, it has often been said that it is impossible to raise a baby seal in captivity. The first difficulty was to get the seals to take milk from a bottle, which is the usual method of hand-rearing baby animals, but for some reason they could not be persuaded to do this. Then somebody experimented by inserting a long tube down the baby seal's throat and into its stomach and then pumping the milk in. As a conseqeuence, several people have now managed to rear baby seals.

26

Seconds out, round one! This baby chimpanzee can hardly wait to meet his opponent

We know that a baby seal grows very fast, and analysis of the mother seal's milk shows it to be very rich. The next problem was to obtain just the right substitute for the milk of the mother. One man has solved this by using the richest cow's milk and adding to each pint 2½ oz. of whale oil, ½ oz. of cod liver oil and one raw egg. This is given to the seal three times a day.

It is supposed that when a baby seal is old enough the mother teaches it to catch fish. What we do not know is how the mother teaches this, or even whether she teaches her baby at all. It may be that a baby seal in its natural habitat learns this by instinct. However, when a baby seal has been successfully reared on its 'stomach pump' the next problem is to wean it. Where this obstacle has been overcome, it has been by the owner of the baby seal patiently forcing fish down its throat until at last the seal gets the idea first of swallowing and then of picking the fish up for itself.

Not all baby animals present as difficult a problem as the seal, but it is nevertheless true to say about the rearing of young animals in captivity, whether it be in a zoo or in a private house or garden, that each species presents us with different problems to solve, and even individuals of the same species differ slightly. It follows, therefore, that there is much trial and error involved, and it seems that some people are better at it than others. Why some people prove better foster-parents is hard to define, but there is at least one thing that can be said: those who make the better foster-parents are quick at divining the day-to-day or even the minute-to-minute needs of their charges. Part of the secret is the ability to learn from the young animal itself what it requires any moment throughout the period of adoption. It is this that convinces me that the natural parents, although guided to a large extent by, what we have called instinct, react also to the demands made upon them by their offspring. Conversely, I feel confident that while the youngster may be guided largely by instinct it is able nevertheless to convey something to the parent, especially in an emergency, of what should be done.

Some years ago I decided I would like to have a tame fox. An advertisement for one appeared in the newspaper, which I answered. The fox advertised was a very young cub of the European red fox. The same kind of fox is found over most of Asia as well, and also in North Africa. Some scientists believe that it belongs to the same species as the American red fox, although others treat these as separate species. Certainly they are very similar both in appearance and habits.

For a long time I had wanted to learn more about this animal which, although spread over half the world and familiar to us from childhood on, is almost a closed book so far as the intimate details of its family life are concerned.

At the same time as I wrote for the cub I asked how it had been fed and what I should need to do for it on arrival. The reply came back that it was still taking milk and needed nothing more. The cub arrived in a box, and when this was opened it started to whine; I promptly fetched it some milk, which it drank. An hour later, although installed comfortably, it seemed restless and continued to call with what can only be described as a bird-like trill, which ended every now and then in a puppy-like whine. This was the first time I had had to deal with a fox cub and I had unwisely sought no help from those who might have had experience of rearing these animals. So I stood looking down

27

The baby gorilla is obviously perplexed, sticking its fingers in its mouth, as a child would

Rhesus monkeys live in troops and the babies not only can play with the mother but with groups of other monkey babies

helplessly at the cub as it walked around and over my feet, trilling and whining. I tried to imagine what a vixen would have done in these circumstances and how she would have interpreted the signs. The cub was trying to give me the answer—not consciously, of course—when it took the cloth of my trouser-leg in its mouth and tugged.

I sat down on a bench and the cub tried to scramble up on to my lap. Finally, I had the wit to pick it up. It reached up as far as it could and succeeded in grasping the lapel of my jacket. It dawned on me that in these circumstances the vixen would have tried to find it some food, and this is what I did. Once the food had been brought there was no longer any doubt. The cub ate ravenously, and when satisfied showed me by its actions that it wanted to be picked up, which I did. It nestled in my hands, its eyelids began to droop, and shortly after it allowed itself to be put into its sleeping-box, where we heard no more of it for several hours.

There was about the cub an alertness, underlined by the pricked ears, sharp muzzle and expressive eyes. There was, too, a seeming purposiveness about every movement, more pronounced than in a puppy or a kitten. There was

28

an appearance of intelligence beyond the capacity of so small and fragile a beast. Above all, the cub appeared to know what it needed beyond the limits of the usual pattern of instinctive actions, and yet, when I came to know foxes better, it could be seen that this cub was behaving true to the pattern of its kind.

In due course the cub grew up and we obtained a vixen for its mate. They had several litters of cubs, and from studying the family life of these foxes I was able later to interpret the experience I have just described. The cub had been fed milk only until the time it came to us, but evidently it had reached

A baboon and her two babies

us at about the time for weaning. When this happens with its normal parents the cub ceases to go to the vixen's teats but reaches up to her mouth and takes solid food from it. This, it seems, is the explanation of its attempting to reach up to my mouth, although it could only reach my lapel.

This is only one example of the kind of simple action of which animals are capable, by which there is an interplay between parent and offspring, making the instincts of each fit like a key into a lock. We may observe animals in the wild and yet fail to see the significance of these actions unless we also have the practical experience of trying to enter into their world by acting as foster-parents. The person who succeeds most with rearing young animals in captivity is the one who is quick at interpreting such signs, especially when that person has knowledge gained from watching animals in the wild. There must also be sympathy, a gentleness of touch combined with firmness, a soothing voice and an ability to avoid any quick movement that might alarm. Young animals also need stroking and fondling as substitutes for the touch of the mother's tongue, and only within the last few years has experiment shown how essential to the future well-being is this attention. Mother-love may be an impalpable

Twins born to Nimmy, a brown bear at Whipsnade Zoo, about to demonstrate a bear dance

quality but it confers a **physical** benefit, as has been demonstrated by experiments on rats.

The method used in the experiments carried out on rats in the United States has been to have animals of the same type and age in separate groups which are housed under identical conditions and given the same food. The only difference between the two groups was that the members of one group were handled daily and those of the other group were not handled. Thus the rats in the second group were ignored except that their basic needs were provided for. When tested for the ability to withstand rigorous conditions and to solve problems it was found that the rats that had been handled daily showed a higher degree of what may, for our purpose, be called intelligence, which expressed itself in a greater ability to solve problems; they were also better able to withstand extremes of temperature and other components of hard living.

The mother animal in the wild confers a considerable amount of licking on her infants, which amounts to a systematic handling and stroking by a human foster-parent. Those who practise massaging the body with the hands as a more or less daily routine will readily concede that this can have a significant effect on one's health and well-being, as well as on one's alertness of mind. Ten minutes' superficial massage of the body each day brings a feeling of well-being and contentment out of proportion to the actions involved or the time taken. No doubt if we did not wear clothes we should all be given to this as a sub-

A calf of the North American bison belonging to a race that was once numbered in its millions and was only preserved by being taken into captivity

The baby nilgai is also known as the young blue bull although it is an antelope. The cow and the bull are sacred to Hindus, and when it was found that the nilgai was becoming rare its name was changed to blue bull to encourage the Hindus not to kill it

conscious action. At all events, there can be no doubt as to the results. It is not surprising then to find that it has been scientifically established that stroking, petting and handling are of benefit to the health and education of a baby animal.

The matter goes further than this, however, since there is one form of licking which is essential for baby animals that spend their early days in the nest. This can be strikingly illustrated by the story of a man who endeavoured to bring up an otter cub knowing nothing at all about otters or the care and rearing of small animals. His method was to give it milk whenever it whimpered. But instead of prospering it began to show signs of discomfort from a belly swollen with food. Fortunately, at this point, the man received a visitor who understood these affairs. She took the young otter, held it over a basin of water and massaged under the cub's tail with a wad of cottonwool moistened with warm water. The cub shortly evacuated its bowel and all was well.

A vixen has her cubs in an earth for about three weeks after they are born and before they come above ground. Yet at no time is the interior of the earth soiled with excreta. The same is true for the nest in which kittens or puppies have passed their early days. This need for sanitation expressed by the mother is not present in those animals such as fawns, foals and calves, or the young leverets which are born at an advanced stage of development and can soon walk. It is the babies born helpless and in a nest of some sort that need the mother's help. She licks the stomach, thereby aiding digestion, and she also licks under the tail, which aids the action of the bowel, and she removes the

31

The birth of a polar bear cub in a zoo is always an event of great interest

Below: the kodiak bear is one of the largest bears in the world, but that is no reason why this cub has to be cheeky about it

excrement at the same time. Some people, when speaking of kittens or puppies, go so far as to speak of the mother 'milking' the babies, which is an expressive phrase that tells us more about this method of sanitation than a multitude of words.

The value of the daily massage as a substitute for the natural mother's attentions was demonstrated in the case of the polar bear cub born in the Prague Zoo in 1942, which was reared by the Superintendent and his wife in their flat. They told how much the cub liked to be combed and brushed, and they found that this not only kept the coat clean but massaged the stomach, encouraged digestion and assisted the motion of the bowels. It also encouraged deep breathing, improved the circulation of the blood and kept the temperature of the body even in all parts.

The experiences gained through the rearing of this cub also indicate another pitfall to be avoided. It is one that would not occur in nature. Because the cub grizzled for more milk even after it had been fed, and because of its winning ways, on one occasion it was given too much milk. Within two days it was so gorged that it became ill. It began to cry continuously, was seized with spasms, its breathing became laboured, its heartbeat irregular, convulsions set in and finally the cub went into a deep faint. This was all the result of gluttony. Fortunately, the symptoms and the cause were recognised, the cub recovered and all was well. For those two days it had taken twice to three times the amount of milk it should have had, which is something that could not happen with the natural mother because she would not have that supply.

Altogether, therefore, since all baby animals do little more than sleep and

32

These two polar bear cubs in a zoo form a pleasing family group as they enjoy lunch-time with their mother

eat for the first part of their lives their requirements are simple. They can be listed as five essentials: food, sleep, warmth, assisted sanitation and a certain amount of coddling, which is mainly given with the mother's tongue. And the main thing to avoid is allowing them to over-eat.

Weaning has been mentioned as a problem for the unnatural parent. Not all baby animals are as difficult about this as the baby seal. Usually the adopted youngster will give some indication itself that the time is approaching when solid food should be taken. The example of the fox cub has been given. Guinea pigs and some of the other smaller animals show the way themselves, as do young rabbits which at a certain time in their early life start to chew grass. They do no more than chew it at first, then spit it out; but when anything of this sort happens, and the young animal starts to chew the nearest available substance, then is the time to make available to it the kind of food it would have in the wild. With young rabbits it is as well to put grass in their feeding quarters some time before they should be weaned, renewing it daily. At the appropriate moment they will start chewing, so indicating that they should be given more. That is the kind of pattern to work to, and there are enough books on the subject to guide us, although they are not necessary if we watch the signs and symptoms.

For the flesh-eaters, the experiences gained with the Prague cub will be sufficient guide. When it was thought that weaning time was near pieces of meat were put in its milk. At first it ignored the meat, or treated it with distaste, at most taking it into the mouth and spitting it out again. Then it started to chew it, but again spat it out. Finally, it took to chewing it and swallowing it.

The lesser panda of the mountain forests of Nepal to Burma always has two young at birth. Until the giant panda found its way to zoos the lesser panda, with its rich chestnut fur and white face, was a popular favourite

The golden hamster was reared in captivity for the first time as recently as 1930; very easily tamed, it has become a popular pet

Foal suckling

learning and instinct

The first essential for any baby is food: the puppy instinctively finds its way to the mother's teats soon after birth

Young kitten against the sunlight

Anyone who has watched a puppy or a kitten grow up, and kept it until old age, will not need telling what changes take place from the helpless baby to the wise old animal. At first all we see is a helpless mite feebly waving its legs but unable to walk, with eyes not yet open, ears still sealed, with very little hair, unable even to keep itself warm, and capable of no more than trying, by its sense of smell, to locate the mother's teats. For the rest it merely sleeps, digests its food, and depends even on the mother for simple sanitation and hygiene. A helpless baby in very truth, and yet containing within itself, like a bud before it begins to open, the seeds of its own development. Then we turn to the mature animal, whether cat or dog, and we see an individual with a marked personality: self-reliant, able to respond to our moods, even able, for all we can tell to the contrary, to read our thoughts, and certainly in many other ways worldly-wise.

The steps by which this transition is accomplished are not clearly marked, because change is going on all through life. But we can list what the factors are that have led to it. They can be conveniently thought of as threefold: instinct, learning and intelligence. This is, however, to simplify the situation over-much, but provided we keep in mind that each of these is in turn made up of several parts no harm will be done. In addition, we have to remember that no one of these can be clearly defined. Instinct, for example, is an overworked word for which no ready definition can be given, although most people have a rough idea of what it means. It is the same with intelligence.

Throughout its life any animal is controlled or influenced by what is happening within its body, and also by what is happening around it. Its whole life is conditioned by automatic processes within the body itself and by what is eaten and what is breathed. The contact with the outside world is through the senses, and is dependent upon what goes on in the world around. One of the first, certainly one of the most obvious, of the automatic internal processes starts when the heart begins to beat, and this happens before birth and continues until death. Breathing is similar except that it starts immediately after birth. This point need not be laboured, except to point out that there are certain other internal processes that are more readily recognised, and are known as reflex actions. The action of the heart and the breathing are in principle the same as those other reflex actions that we can see, so it is best to illustrate all of them with the reflex actions that are stimulated from outside. Thus if somebody throws a ball of paper at your face you blink. A baby will do the same, because this is something that requires no thought and no learning. The reflex is inborn. The sight of something travelling towards the eye causes

A questioning expression from a floppy-eared puppy

A boxer pup wishing he was away from it all

a message to travel to the brain, and the return message sets the muscles of the eyelids to work. Within the body itself there are chemical substances poured into the blood from glands, which act as messengers. These are what make the body tick.

Later, when once a ball has been thrown at your head and you have felt the impact of it and are hurt, you learn something. You learn to duck or dodge the next time. This is something learned, it is an experience, but the response to it has become automatic. Apply this to baby animals—say, a puppy. Some misguided people throw stones at dogs. The first time a puppy experiences this it is taken unawares, simply because it has not met this situation before. But even as a puppy it soon learns to associate with pain not only the stone travelling towards it but a person stooping to pick something off the ground, and at the sight of this it runs away. Once having had the experience the puppy will run away even if the person is only stooping to tie his shoelace. This means using energy for no purpose, whereas if a dog could think it would be more inclined to run away only when it was obvious that the person was picking

The familiar picture of a kitten chasing a ball of wool is an illustration of a flesh-eating animal taking its first lessons in hunting

up a stone, not otherwise. However, this is playing safe, and safety is important in the life of a baby animal especially.

The dog and the stone illustrates a simple form of learning, and similar things are happening all the time in the baby animal's world and, indeed, throughout the lifetime of the individual. It is the way it learns to avoid danger or injury, and also it is a means whereby the young animal is taught. A good example of how an animal learns is seen in the training of a baby hippopotamus.

One of the chief dangers a baby hippo has to face is from an old male hippo, who may even be its father. The baby may meet him either on land or in water, and the only protection it has is from its mother. In the water the baby hippo is taught to swim at its mother's shoulder because in that position the mother can quickly move from one side of her baby to the other, to place herself between an attacking male and her infant. On land hippos follow paths through the tall grass. Then the danger will be of encountering a male coming from the opposite direction, or there may be the danger of meeting a lion. At any rate, the best defensive position for the youngster is behind its mother. So

39

the baby hippo is taught these two positions early in life in this way: the mother, using her ponderous snout, edges the baby to where it should be. If it strays from this position it is edged back, and this happens again and again until it 'gets the idea'. Once it has learned to do this and then disobeys, or if it proves a bad pupil and slow to learn, the mother may punish it by belabouring it with her snout until the youngster squeals. If it moves into the correct position, the mother will turn and lick it. It is a system of punishment for doing wrong, and reward, by bestowing affection, for doing right.

The baby hippo is taught by the mother to keep near her shoulder while they are in the water

From this simple example, there emerges another factor in learning. The baby hippo 'gets the idea'. This is a figure of speech used for something we cannot fully understand, much less explain, which is called insight behaviour. We see it in ourselves, and we see it in animals; it is rather like the ability to judge distances and heights in that it does not necessarily come at once, nor does it depend on precise thinking, nor is it inborn. A young fox cub, soon after it had come above ground, ran at a branch lying on the ground and tried to jump over it, landing with its fat little belly across the branch and its legs

40

sprawled. It struggled over, but the next time this was attempted it jumped the branch with ease. Here was insight, in that the cub had formed the idea that it would jump over the branch, but this needed to be reinforced by learning. Another form of insight behaviour is when a puppy, without having seen a latch before, lifts it with its tongue in order to open a gate. It takes in the situation at a glance and solves a problem without obvious signs of having to make any mental effort.

However, whenever we are talking about animal behaviour we are speaking very largely on the basis of supposition. Even those most expert in this new science tend to shift their ground from time to time, or to put forward views which they reject later or which other experts refuse to accept. There are anomalies in the behaviour of the animals themselves. One of the more surprising is seen in otters, which readily learn to walk, and we expect them to learn to swim readily, as indeed they do—once they start. Yet the baby otter does not, like the proverbial duck, take to water but has to be coaxed in by its mother. Exactly how she does this is very difficult to describe. There is a mixture of action and reaction between parent and infant, the end result of which is the young otter enters the water. Or again, the baby hippo, normally born near water, will enter it if danger is near (or it tends to do so), and yet there have been occasions when the mother hippo has been seen to encourage the baby on to her back, after which she gives a heave and tips the babe into the water, as if forcing it to take to its future home. This suggests that fear may often be an excellent educator.

It is sometimes said of the California sea lion that in spite of its grace in the water the baby has to learn to swim, and that the mother picks the pup up by the scruff and carries it to the water for its first swimming lesson. The pup struggles in the surf at first, although it later learns to ride the waves as easily as its parents. Experience in the field, as well as experimentation in the laboratory, has shown that a baby seal of any kind, whether a hair seal, sea lion or fur seal, automatically makes swimming movements as soon as it is immersed in water, and will do so when it is so near to being dead that it can

It didn't break! A look of disappointment from a thirsty kitten

have no consciousness of what it is doing. In laboratory tests even an anaesthetised baby seal will make these swimming movements. The sea lion and the fur seal, unlike the hair seals, will take their babes by the scruff to lift them up the beach away from dangerous boulders or pounding surf, and people seeing this have jumped wrongly to the conclusion that the mother was taking the pup to water.

We are on more certain ground in dealing with another aspect of animal behaviour. This is in the field of what are called sign stimuli, which may operate through one or other of the senses; the reaction on the part of the individual receiving the stimuli can be forecast because there is an inborn pattern of response. A simple example would be when a dog, a wolf, or even a fox, growls at its offspring and causes it to stop short, realising that this is a danger signal: if it continues what it is doing it will be either in danger from an enemy or from punishment from the parent. Most animals give warning of peril to their youngsters by some kind of call, and the youngster's inborn reaction is to obey. It is, however, only a step from this to actual punishment, and in some instances it is difficult to draw the line between a sign stimulus and chastisement. There was, for example, an occasion when a puppy was stealing from the food bowl of a grown dog. The puppy was taking all the choice pieces, and, in fact, every time the dog went to take a juicy piece of food the puppy took it from under his nose. The dog bore this with patience, but

In this sequence of photographs the first minutes of a zebra's life are shown. For a while he seems to be resting, probably gaining strength for those first few wobbly steps. The young zebra is ready to walk away behind his mother only twenty minutes after he is born

clearly his patience was being sorely tried. Finally, he put his mouth to the puppy's ear and gave a particularly hollow bark, an explosive bark such as is seldom heard from any dog. The puppy was startled out of its wits. It raced away from the bowl and literally ran round in circles, yelling piteously all the time.

The puppy in this story was rather more than a baby, and the same can be said for several of the other animals we have been discussing. Before going further, therefore, it might be as well to define what we mean by a 'baby' animal.

We recognise several stages in the lifetime of an animal, and we give them labels such as baby, infant, sub-adult and adult. The last of these is the only one for which the definition is clear and unambiguous: it is the stage when the animal is capable of mating, although it may not by then have attained full size. The sub-adult is an animal that is only approaching full size and is coming into breeding condition but is not sexually mature. The borderline between the adult and the sub-adult is not a hard and fast line, and that between the infant and the sub-adult is even less so. The period of the sub-adult might, for the sake of convenience, be defined as the time when the young animal is no longer dependent upon the parent and before it has yet become sexually mature or fully grown.

The term 'baby animal' is the least satisfactory of all, because the only definition we could give that would meet all requirements would be for that stage when the young animal is completely helpless, and, as we shall later see, some animals are helpless only for seconds after being born. Such a definition obviously applies to a baby cat, dog, fox or bear, but it is almost impossible to speak of a baby guinea pig, and even more impossible for some other species.

Young guinea pigs are highly precocious, able to run almost from birth and able to start chewing at two to three days old

Right: chipmunk mother gathers food

44

Young grey squirrels

Young wild rabbits

A family of golden hamsters ready for a foraging expedition

The hide of the black rhino is actually dark brown. Here a mother keeps watch with her calf

The newly born guinea pig is able to run about almost at birth, and it starts chewing solid food within two or three days of being born. It may not swallow the chewed food at first, but at least it is learning to feed even at this very early age.

Even this is not a record of precocious behaviour. The guinea pig is a South American rodent and one of its near relations is the agouti. The adult agouti looks more like a small tail-less antelope, a resemblance which is heightened by its having three toes on the hind-foot, each toe bearing a hoof-like claw. The young agouti is able to run about almost within seconds of birth and is able to chew leaves within an hour of birth. The young American tree porcupine is, if anything, more precocious still. Although it is two days after birth before it can eat leaves, by that time it is able to climb trees to get them.

We are so used to the human baby, which does not take solid food until it has enough teeth to chew it, that it is natural to suppose the number of the teeth at birth or soon after might serve as a guide to whether an animal will suck for a longer or shorter period. This, however, is not so. A piglet possesses teeth even when being suckled, and in domestic pigs this can often be the cause of damage to the sow. Nor is the size of the adult animal any guide, although at first sight there may appear to be a relation between the size of the mother and the length of time she nurses her babies. Most baby mice and rats suck for ten to twenty days after birth, but the young of the guinea pig, the adult of which is slightly larger than the brown rat, will start chewing at two to three days old, as we have seen. Then the agouti, as we know, which is the size of a hare or a small antelope, will start chewing within an hour. Finally, we have the walrus, the adult of which weighs over a ton, whose young continue to be

Baby European woodmice being nursed by their mother

Baby house mice in the nest
still blind and unable to hear

suckled for nearly two years. As a rough guide it could be said that the larger the adult the longer the young is likely to be suckled, but this rule is not always applicable.

The comparison between the European rabbit and the European brown hare brings this out clearly. The two are closely related, they look alike and their way of life is very similar. Yet in these two species the early stages of the young are strikingly different. At birth the rabbit is blind, deaf and naked, and is able to make no more than the feeblest movements with its limbs. It is born in a nest at the blind end of a special burrow, which slopes down from the entrance so that the nest end is a few inches below the ground. The nest is lined with fur, plucked by the doe from her own breast with her teeth. The baby rabbit does not open its eyes and ears until the eighth day, and by then is has grown a short coat of fur. At that age it can move about, but it cannot hop because its hind-legs move independently of each other, and it does not come above ground until it is three weeks old.

By way of contrast, the brown hare is born with eyes and ears open and with a short coat of fur. It is able soon after birth to move about, and it rests in a depression in the grass, where the mother visits it to suckle it. And whereas the young rabbit is not independent until fifty to sixty days old, the young hare achieves independence in about a month.

The young Nigerian hare can look after itself almost from the time of birth except that its mother must suckle it

A trial of strength between two lively, three-month-old bear cubs

There is one more marked difference between the baby rabbit and baby hare which will be dealt with in a moment. Meanwhile, it is of interest to consider how the jack rabbits and other rabbits of North America fill the gap between them. The jack rabbit is a hare in the European sense, but the mother jack rabbit treats her litter somewhat differently from the European hare. The litter usually numbers four, but may contain up to six babies, born with a mottled brownish fur and eyes fully open. They are able to suck within five minutes of birth, and they are born in a nest of grass and fur, the mother covering them with some of the fur whenever she leaves the nest. The cottontail, or molly, which is much more like the European rabbit, has babies that are blind, helpless and naked, born into a nest that is no more than a depression in the ground lined with grass and fur. Like the young European rabbits the eyes of the young cottontails open later, but not until the age of ten days.

One of the more striking differences between the European rabbit and the European hare lies in the way they control their body temperature in the early days of life. The warm nest and the warmth from the mother's body are a necessity for the growth of the baby rabbit. This much we may infer, although we cannot be wholly certain, from what is known of the young rat, which is also born into a warm nest and warmed by the mother's body. The young rat, although normally kept warm in this way, can behave like a hibernating animal when forced to do so. It can relinquish its temperature-control if exposed to cold air and almost stop breathing, so much so that it is able under experimental conditions to survive for nearly two hours in an atmosphere devoid of oxygen. After the age of ten days, when it has a coat of hair to help retain the heat of the body, it loses this ability.

This apparent paradox merely means that a young rat—and presumably a young rabbit—must be kept warm in order to grow at the normal rate, but can survive exposure to cold for a while by what is almost suspended animation, although during these periods growth is arrested.

The young of the brown bears and of the American black bear are very small at birth, about one two-hundredth the size of the mother. They are so small and helpless that they appear to be little balls of flesh, which is why it used to be believed that the mother, when she licked them, was licking them into shape. They behave in the early stages of life much as the young rabbit and rat do with regard to body temperatures.

A baby dik-dik, one of the smallest antelopes, still all legs but very much on the alert for every disturbance of the undergrowth in which it has been born

The differences between the young of the hoofed animals also bear out the point that there is no rigid relationship between the size of the adult and the behaviour of their newly born youngsters. The baby chamois can rise on to its feet and walk slowly a few seconds after birth and while it is still wet. It starts to eat grass at ten days but continues to suck until two months old. The young giraffe can get on to its feet five minutes after being born, but the young of the roe deer, which is more the size of the chamois, makes no attempt to stand for an hour after birth.

Were we to deal strictly with 'baby animals' we should have to confine our attention to instinct purely: to reflex actions and innate reactions to sign stimuli. Even the fact that guinea pigs and others chew at such an early age is not a matter of learning. Probably, although this would need proving, such animals start to use their teeth either at the sight of food or at the smell of it, in which event we should speak of the food constituting a sign stimulus. More likely, the need for the jaws to be moved and the teeth to bite springs from a spontaneous impulse like the one that sets the heart beating or the lungs working. Certainly in actual babyhood there is little which happens that can be called learning. This comes at a later stage and increases in intensity in the

Left: a young African elephant finds an ideal solution to the heat problem under its obliging mother

Right: the giraffe's main foe is the lion, against which the mother will defend her baby with her powerful hoofs. All the same, the baby giraffe is able to raise itself on its feet within five minutes of birth

Below: the polar bear cub decides to join its mother in a nap

infant stage, and more especially once the infant has left the parents when it is sub-adult. But if the infant were left entirely without guidance until the moment it left its mother and started to fend for itself, the likelihood is that few indeed would ever survive the dangers and hazards of life. That is where play comes in, as we shall see in the next chapter. Play helps to knit together the reflexes and the instincts, it adds new tricks to the repertoire, and with learning and memory reinforcing these equips the young animal for a life of independence. It is then, also, during the play period of life, that anything which could be called intelligence begins to show itself.

Measuring intelligence in animals is a problem which has absorbed scientists through the ages; their experiments have very often produced results which illuminate the subject of human intelligence.

A very young foal with protective mother

56

A young raccoon goes exploring

Right: young beaver

A contented sun bear sucking his foot to pass the time

A cautious fox cub half hidden in the undergrowth. Fox cubs are completely dependent on their parents for some weeks and do not fend for themselves until five or six months old

You and I and anyone who has pets, whether kittens or puppies or any other animals, say that we watch them playing. It is not unusual to find that when somebody is writing about wild animals he will say, as likely as not, that they are playful, or he will use such phrases as 'when they are at play'. Yet the scientist who studies animal behaviour has somewhat different views. Either he will refuse to recognise that animals play at all or he will grudgingly admit that such animals as apes and monkeys may play, but no others, or he will seek to describe in entirely different terms what ordinary people call play. In short, the non-scientist believes that animals do play, and will say so without a blush; the scientist says they do not play, at least not in the same way as people play.

This seeming clash of views is not as serious as it may appear, nor is there so great a gulf between these two sets of ideas. Certainly animals do not play in the same way that adult humans do: their play is not organised, nor does it follow rules in the same way, but this we should hardly expect. If, however, we concentrate our attention on the way children play, either when they are on their own or when two or more are left to their own devices, then we find that what they do is not so very different from the play of animals. For example, when two squirrels are playing they will dodge each other round the base of a tree in exactly the same way that very young children do. Kittens, puppies and even the young of wild animals brought up as pets, will carry out a performance that looks very like the simple hide-and-seek young children play. Moreover, all play in this way on their own initiative, without our teaching them to do so. When we watch young animals carefully we not infrequently find them doing something that looks very like the game children play, which some people call 'tag' and others call 'touch-you-last'. Finally, a game very much like 'king-of-the-castle' can be seen played by several different kinds of young animals.

Before considering the meaning of play it may be worth looking at some of the antics of what is probably the most playful of animals, the squirrel, especially the grey or Carolina squirrel. Normally we see it running over the ground or through the trees going about its ordinary business of food-gathering. On rare occasions a grey squirrel may be seen soaring through the air from tree-top to tree-top, looking the picture of grace and as if it were thoroughly enjoying the experience. The best time to see it is, however, in the early morning, just after dawn when nobody is about, so that the squirrel is completely undisturbed. This illustrates one of the first principles of play, that it is something indulged in when there is an absence of overriding care. The squirrel is

Right: the fox cub as it was on arrival, weary and not sure about its new home and in no mood for play. A young animal must feel secure before it is ready to play

Right: when a cub opens its mouth like this it is ready for play

Below: a group of young foxes at play; they mostly play in couples but at times get together for a free-for-all rough and tumble

a good subject because it not only plays when young but all through its life until it begins to suffer from old age. This gives us ample time to study its play.

The evolutions and gyrations of which a squirrel is capable can be divided under two headings. There are those that are associated with the normal activities of life, and there are those that seem to bear no relation to them. Under the first heading comes what may be called the wheel action. Years ago it was a common practice to put a wheel in the cage in which a tame squirrel was kept. The squirrel would run round and round in the wheel interminably, and so has arisen the phrase, used to describe a person who is very busy but getting nowhere, 'going round like a squirrel in a cage'.

To put this in correct perspective we have to trace what happens under varying conditions. A squirrel in a small cage will go round and round in a wheel. A squirrel in a larger cage, but without a wheel, will spend a lot of time jumping at the side of the cage, leaping from there to the roof, then to the other side and down again to the ground, repeating this again and again. It is performing a wheel action. Put the squirrel in a large aviary with branches arranged to represent its natural habitat and it will perform an even larger

wheel action, using the branches, and from this we can see that it is doing no more than it would in the wild if it were free to race around the branches of trees, but because it is restricted the circuit it follows must of necessity be roughly a circle. The smaller the cage, and the less room in which to move, the more this circuit corresponds to a true circle, until finally, in a very small cage, the animal uses a wheel as a substitute for the wide open spaces.

This kind of movement is not true play, and it is this behaviour that the scientist has in mind when he declares that squirrels do not play in our sense of the word. On the other hand, if a squirrel is given a fir cone or some other round object, it will play with it as a child would play with a ball; it will throw it about, dribble it along the ground, hug it and turn a somersault over it, and go through many evolutions of this kind. This playing with a fir cone bears no relation to anything it does in the ordinary course of serious living, and is therefore very near to what we call recreation, or true play. On very rare occasions a squirrel in the wild has been seen bowling a nut with its paws, and this must be called play also, because in normal circumstances a nut represents something that must either be eaten or buried, both of which represent for the squirrel serious purpose in life.

Play in kittens is so proverbial that we even talk about 'kittenish play' when grown people are being childish

62

Almost as if seeing its quarry before it, the young puma stalks imaginary prey

An example of an unusual animal friendship. After being suckled by its foster mother a young baby leopard expresses its thanks

Sometimes a squirrel, both in captivity and in the wild, has been seen holding a stick in its fore-paws and turning somersaults over it, as a gymnast turns somersaults over a horizontal bar. This could be true play, and certainly looks like it, but it could also be interpreted as simulating the squirrel's normal movements of clambering around the thinner branches on a tree.

We can now understand what the scientists have to say about the significance of these activities you and I call play. One writer defined play as the manifestation of instincts before the animal really needs them: that is, play emerges like any other instinct but before its time, so that in a manner of speaking the young animal can practise being grown-up. Another theory is that play is the premonition of serious activities to come, and that far from getting rid of superfluous energy the play exercises develop the muscles and joints in preparation for serious activities in later life. Other ideas are that play enables an animal to become acquainted with its surroundings, with the world into which it has been born; and that play is pleasurable, and being pleasurable it is a valuable stimulus to learning. Finally, there is the view that play has all the components of a single instinct and that the movements carried out in the course of it later subserve combat, self-defence, escape and reproduction.

None of these seems unreasonable, so it becomes very much a matter of opinion which is the more likely to represent the truth. The last of these theories gains considerable support from what has been learned about play in fox cubs. Usually there are three or four cubs in a litter, and once they come above ground these play a great deal among themselves and with their parents. Their play then is, to all intents and porposes, a mad rough-and-tumble in which it is difficult to see any order.

I had reason to think otherwise when I reared tame foxes, and it was fortunate, perhaps, that the first was a cub on its own. I took charge of it just as it was at the weaning stage, although it had been hand-fed with milk for several weeks before by its previous owner, who had rescued it when it was a very small baby. The cub must have been at about the age when it would first have come above ground had it been with its natural parents. It did little more than feed and sleep at first, but such time as was spent otherwise was occupied in seizing objects that could be gripped by the teeth and shaking them. It had no use for a ball, and seemed not to have any inclination to chase it or pick it up. Its favourite toy was a piece of cloth, which it would seize and worry until tired of that pastime. Anything that could be tested with the teeth soon became ornamented with tooth-marks, and the highest mark of affection it bestowed on its human guardian was to take an outstretched finger in its mouth, bite it gently and then lick it with a velvet-smooth tongue. It would also roll on to its back and, with open jaws, invite a rough-and-tumble, which meant rolling it back and forth on its back, or rolling it right over.

There came the time when it was markedly more active, and during this

These baby cheetahs have not yet got the long legs of their parents and play is essential to develop and strengthen their legs

The cub has seized its mother's tail, just as a kitten might pounce on a rolling ball of wool

64

period I settled down to watch its behaviour and note what it did. The whole story would take too long to tell, but briefly it amounted to this: that for about a fortnight it performed a few play actions which it repeated each day. At the end of that time the pattern changed more or less abruptly. It was as if the cub was practising new tricks, although there was about it all the time a spirit of fun, or so it seemed. During this second period, in addition to the new tricks one could see every so often one or more of the tricks of the first fortnight being performed, as if the cub were refreshing its memory. At the end of about another two weeks the pattern changed again, and as with the second period the tricks from the previous periods would be intermingled occasionally with the new tricks.

At about the time that I was making my observations of the fox cub at play, mice were being studied elsewhere along similar lines, not in relation to play but to the way the mice developed from birth onwards. There also it was found that the emergence of their behaviour patterns took place in regular stages, just as I had seen in the fox. The antics of the fox, which everyone calls play and which looked so much like pure play, follow the same development as other bodily activities, including those arising from pure instinct.

It seems a little depressing to have to regard play as an instinct instead of a light-hearted enjoyment, but there is another side to it which we shall come to in a moment. Meanwhile, there are a few more comments to be made on the behaviour of the young fox. There was the time, when he was first with me, when he did little more than feed, sleep and grip things with his teeth, to chew

them or worry them. This is so like what the baby rabbit or baby guinea pig does at that stage that a direct comparison cannot be avoided. The rabbit or the guinea pig chews grass but does not swallow it. The instinct to chew is displayed without the need to swallow what has been chewed. With the fox, the instinct to bite and worry has emerged without the experience of hunting.

Later when the fox was grown and had a mate as well as his own cubs, I used to watch these cubs playing. Had I not watched their father closely when he was a cub their play would have seemed no more than a jumbled rough-and-tumble. However, I was able to see that they were doing exactly the same things, but doing them in pairs. For example, when the cub lay on his back with legs in the air and mouth wide open inviting me to play with him (as I thought), he was doing the same as a pair of cubs will do, but the other cub of the pair was missing. Frequently one sees one cub on its back with the other straddling it and sparring with its open mouth.

The cub when on its own would often dash across the pen and turn a complete somersault halfway. It seems difficult to interpret this in any other way than as a manifestation of high spirits or as a method of getting rid of superfluous energy, or even as pure fun. Another game young foxes play looks like 'king-of-the-castle': one stands on a knoll or a log and the other dances around it on the ground beneath, feinting at it with open mouth as if seeking to dislodge it. After a while the two change places. This game is played by cubs and also by adults, but with adults this appears to be part of the courtship. Whether indulged in by the cubs or the adults, this also is a matter of pure fun. Yet, if we recall one of the definitions given of play earlier in this chapter, we could say that the play of fox cubs, in this instance at least, consists of 'movements carried out [which] later subserve reproduction', since even if the courtship does contain elements of sheer frolic these are the preliminary to mating.

There is still the possibility that the same actions could be described as play under certain conditions but as something other than play under another set of conditions. Perhaps a better example can be seen in the play of calves. The commonest manifestations of play in cattle, whether of calves or grown cattle, are trotting, capering or galloping, with the tail held at varying angles; bucking with both hind-feet jerked up behind, often to one side with a lateral twist of the hind-quarters; kicking with one hind-foot at stationary or moving objects; butting with the head or prancing with the head lowered; side-to-side shaking or tossing of the head, and snorting and uttering a sharp baa-ock. In addition, there may be goring movements with head and horns against soft materials like loose soil or hay. This is how calves play and it is also how cows play, especially when they are first let out to grass after having been in stable all winter.

All these movements will be of value to the calf when it grows up for combat, defence and escape from enemies—or they would be if, like its ancestors, the calf were living in the wild. Nevertheless, when cows behave this way after having been in the stable, the movements could be interpreted as an expression of pleasure at being able to move about freely, at being in the light once more and among fresh grass, breathing freely once again—for, whatever we may say, being in a stable even if for the cow's own good means imprisonment, and no prisoner can feel completely carefree.

American black bear cubs learning to climb

A pause to look around before
the brown bear cubs turn on
each other with open mouths
in a snarling bout of play

Left: it is proverbial that the adult goat is all 'butt', and even as kids butting with the forehead is a conspicuous feature of their play

Above: in its most obnoxious mood the adult skunk gives warning of what is to come by raising its tail erect—and even the baby does this in play

Left: rough and tumble between the first giant panda to be born in captivity (at Peking Zoo) and its mother

Right: a plea for help from an over-adventurous kitten marooned on a branch

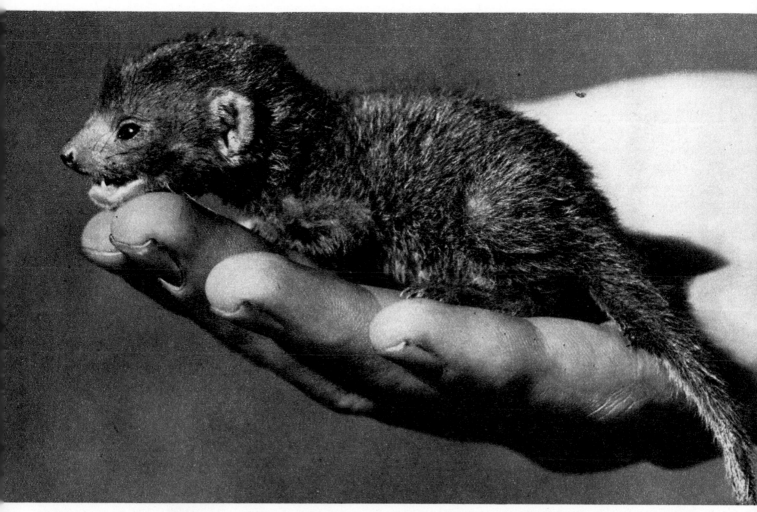

Above: a pygmy mongoose very much at the kitten stage and before it has reached the stage of vigorous romping

The scientist who studied play in calves remarked that cattle enjoyed their play, and even the English, who are said to take their pleasures sadly, never play except to enjoy it. The same scientist found that calves tend to play best in one chosen place in a field, and if confined to a stable yard would do their best to reach this place in order to play. In other words, the calves had a favourite playground.

This leads us to dolphins, which in the last twenty years have been kept in large seaquaria in the United States. Among other things their play has been extensively studied. The scientists watching these dolphins have come to the conclusion that they not only play with each other for the fun of it, but tease the sharks and turtles kept in the same large tanks. The dolphins learn games from their attendants such as retrieving beach-balls or old tyres. They practise these as if trying to perfect their performances, and, more surprising still, will initiate games with their attendants. Balancing small objects on the ends of their snouts is a very common trick with dolphins, and they do this of their own free will.

The most playful of all is the common dolphin, which is the one most commonly seen at sea and on the sea's surface. So far, little attention has been paid to the scientific study of wild common dolphins, but there was an occasion when I watched a school of them off the coast of Cornwall. The dolphins often passed that part of the coast, well out to sea. Then one day as they came in sight the leading dolphin half leapt from the water and fell back in again with a smack, throwing a huge wave out to either side. This seemed to be a signal, for the school altered course and entered the bay.

There, at the foot of the vertical cliff on which I was standing, they played for about half an hour, performing all manner of evolutions. They leapt from the water, stood on their heads with only their tails out of water, swam upside-down just below the surface, and in fact seemed to be trying to swim in every imaginable position. At times, half a dozen of them would line up in a row and, keeping perfect formation, swim forward together, only to break off at the end of the short swim, each going back to its individual tricks. The play ended as abruptly as it began, after which the school swam away out to sea and were soon lost to sight. Most important of all, I had been expecting to see this—indeed had been watching and waiting for it, because I had been told that the dolphins seemed to make a practice of coming into that particular bay to play. Unless I am much mistaken, they treated that bay as their playground, to which they kept returning.

An attractive lion cub readily gives a cheeky smile for the camera

It may be useful to return to the wheel play which was described for the squirrel, because this is something several animals carry out, and in doing so also give evidence of using a favourite playground. The young of the flesh-eaters, such as the dog, cat and fox, as well as the adults, are renowned for their playfulness.

It has been found that the smaller carnivores, such as the stoat, weasel, mink, marten and others of similar size, are even more playful. A tame stoat, kept in a cage and let out into the room at certain times of the day for exercise, also played at intervals during the night when shut up in its cage. It performed very much like a squirrel in a small cage, bounding from one spot to another in a circular movement. It did this with such regularity and precision, putting its feet on the same spots each time, that eventually the wooden floor, sides and roof of the cage became stained at these points, giving a clear record of the movement—an irregular circle.

Mice kept in a roomy cage decorated with grass and pieces of bark to represent their natural habitat will choose a piece of bark or some other object

Growla, a two-month-old Syrian bear cub

70

that has a space beneath it; they will run over the bark to its edge, disappear beneath it to come out at the opposite side, run over the top of the bark once more, and so on, round and round, in a circular movement. Young and old alike will do this, so it is but a short step to running in a wheel. Mice run enormous distances daily over their territories when free in the fields or gardens, and when they are kept in a cage, even if this is a large cage, they make up for their inability to run long distances by running in circles, just as people on an ocean voyage, unable to take walks through the countryside, walk round and round on deck.

An experiment which demonstrates this activity was set up with a wheel in the cage of some zebra mice from West Africa that had not been caged before. In due course these had a litter, so there were young mice as well. Both young and old played with the wheel, but they did not run inside it as they were expected to do. Their behaviour with the wheel gave the impression that they used it as a toy. When the wheel was first put into their cage the mice came out to inspect it. One of them touched it with a paw; the wheel turned slightly and squeaked; both mice ran for cover. After an interval of a few minutes they came out again, inspected it, touched it, and again bolted for cover when it squeaked. Soon, however, they grew familiar with it and started to turn it. They did not run inside it but turned it with the paws, standing on one hind-foot and spinning the wheel with both front paws and the other hind paw. Sometimes the male alone, sometimes the female only would turn it for a while, or the two might stand side by side turning it, changing from one hind paw to the other from time to time. A counting device was fastened to the wheel, and this showed that in one week the mice turned the wheel about 100,000 times, or 15,000 times a day.

When the youngsters were born and had grown sufficiently to leave the nest they also played on the wheel. At first they ran round inside it, but soon they were doing as their parents had done, turning it by standing on the outside. They became so obsessed with the wheel that when playing with it they broke off only long enough to snatch a hasty bite of food. No doubt, if they could, they would have made the mouse equivalent of sandwiches, so as not to interrupt their game!

A not-so-friendly expression from a young tiger

The baby aardwolf, although belonging to the order of flesh-eaters, will find its food among soft-bodied insects because even when grown it has very poor and weak teeth. As an infant it has no defence, nor can its mother defend it against attack, and this is one reason why the aardwolf as a whole is in danger of extinction

'First catch your hare', and if it happens to be a young one, or leveret, you may be surprised at the results. We know that leverets settle into a form soon after being born. The form is no more than a depression in the grass, usually in a tussock or patch of long grass, so that as the leveret crouches in its form the long grass rises on either side of it. Even if it does not conceal the young hare, at least it camouflages its outline and is astonishingly difficult to see; you can spend several hours walking back and forth across a stretch of grassland where hares are known to be, without seeing one. On the other hand, you may see one by accident almost immediately you start to search. A lot depends on how experienced you are at this kind of searching. (In the United States hares are called jack rabbits and young cottontails are sometimes called fawns.)

It is as if the leveret is aware of this difficulty in finding it, for it crouches motionless and usually does not move until you are almost on top of it. Then it dashes away like the wind. And as often as not it is the sight of a leveret running away that gives the first clue to the exact location of its resting place. Remaining motionless without the slightest movement is known as freezing, an expressive phrase which means adopting suddenly a posture of complete immobility and holding it as long as necessary. The leveret does not have to learn these tactics. Freezing is instinctive, and quite a number of young animals use it as the first line of defence.

When an action is instinctive it is normally adopted as the result of some signal from the surrounding world. This signal is a sign stimulus, which we have already discussed. In this instance a large object moving towards a leveret crouched in its form is the sign stimulus, or signal, received through the eye, which sets in motion certain nervous reactions, and these in turn control the movements of the muscles. Theoretically, once a sign stimulus has been received and the innate response—or instinctive action—set in motion, that response should continue as long as the sign stimulus is being received. That, however, would often lead to disaster. If a leveret were crouched in its form and froze at the sight of an approaching fox there would come the moment, as the fox drew near, when it would pick up the scent of the young hare, and that would be that. So we find that when danger draws very close another instinct comes into play—the instinct to flee, and this the leveret does.

Even instinctive action can sometimes be mistimed, or may not fit in with the circumstances. As a consequence the young hare can find itself face to face with an enemy. In such circumstances it may leap, rather like a toad, at whatever has disturbed it, growling and trying to bite, the very reverse of the picture we usually have of the 'timid' hare. The young of the brown hare

of Europe is not the only one to try to defend itself. The jack rabbits in North America rear up on their hind-legs and box with their front paws. Later when the jack rabbit has grown up it loses its defensive display, although the jack hares, as the males are called, do something very like it in the courting season, and the mother has been known to stand up and box the snout of a cow tnat was foraging too near where her babies were lying hidden, and even attack the legs of a man who was approaching too close.

In some animals this defence reaction is seen in the young but disappears as they grow up, in others the defence reaction persists. There is in this an interesting contrast between the hedgehog of the Old World and the porcupine of the New World. Most animal mothers will defend their babies. This is especially true of the flesh-eaters, possibly because their killnig instincts are well developed, but more especially because their teeth and claws are formidable. Nobody in his senses will risk going near a lion cub when the lioness is around, or even, having handled a cub, allow her to get the scent of it on him. Even the wildcat, little larger than the domestic tabby, is a veritable fury in defence of its kittens. There are, however, a few animal mothers that do nothing to

The keen senses and fast speed of the coyote enable it to live successfully in its wilderness range of North America

73

A family of young coyotes in
their rocky nursery in a state
of alarm

Elephant mother and baby

defend their young, and the hedgehog is one. When danger threatens, the
mother hedgehog simply follows her normal routine and rolls up, presenting
a palisade of spines to an intruder. Her babies cannot even shelter under the
mother, and in the early days of life are unable to roll up, even although their
spines may have hardened. Their defence is to bounce into the air. A baby
hedgehog no more than two or three inches long may bounce up as much as
three inches. When one goes to pick up a baby hedgehog, unaware of this
defence mechanism, the impact of the sharp ends of the spines on the finger-tips
can produce discomfort that lasts for quite a while. It is easy to see that a fox
or a badger, poking its nose into a hedgehog's nest and receiving the brunt
of these spines on the sensitive skin of the neb may well be deterred from
attacking further, unless it is very hungry. As the young hedgehog grows up
it loses this particular defence mechanism.

The bouncing action of the baby hedgehog is purely instinctive. This much
is made clear when we watch two or more of them running around together.
If one of them brushes its spines against another the latter will bounce into
the air just as vigorously as it would if an enemy had touched it. Or both of
those that have collided may bounce in unison, presenting a comic sight. The
baby hedgehog never learns to do otherwise, or to discriminate between friend
and foe.

The porcupine's quills are formidable. They are longer and more numerous
in the porcupines of the Old World, but the American porcupine makes the
fullest use of those it has. If an enemy approaches it raises its quills, arches
its back, raises its tail slightly and lowers its nose under its body. The baby

74

porcupine does this as well, which recalls a similar situation in cats. Both the truly wild cat kittens and those of the domestic cat gone wild will bare their teeth and hiss, and doubtless both could inflict painful wounds were they to use the teeth, but the kittens of the feral domestic cat, although showing fight in this way, will calm down and allow themselves to be handled, provided one knows how to deal with them. Domestication has not quenched the instinct to show fight, but generations of selective breeding has inhibited the actual biting.

For the most part young animals depend on their mothers for defence even if they are able to make some slight contribution towards it, as when a fawn responds to the mother's whistle by freezing and lying crouched in the bracken where it is hidden. The giraffe will fight desperately in defence of her baby, striking out with her strong hind-legs and heavy hoofs at an attacking lion. Lions do kill young giraffes, even a grown giraffe occasionally, but usually it takes more than one to do so, and in general the scales are weighted against the lion, who risks having his teeth knocked out.

African antelopes usually run away at the sight of a wild dog or pack of hyenas, and certainly do so on getting the scent of a lion; but they return to

Above and left: members of the cat family learn to show their teeth and spit when very young, like these baby leopards expressing disapproval of the photographer

Right: a young bobcat looks down from a rocky vantage point. Although small, bobcats are fierce and kill many young deer

the attack again and again to protect their young from these very foes during those vital first few hours when the youngster may have learned to stand on its own feet but cannot easily keep up with the herd. There is probably no animal less likely to turn on a beast of prey than a rabbit, and for some reason we do not fully understand a rabbit becomes paralysed even at the presence of a stoat or weasel. Yet a doe rabbit with her babies was seen on one occasion to lash out with her hind feet and send a stoat hurtling through the air to land a full sixteen feet away.

77

The baby hedgehog is born with few spines — and its ability to roll up comes well after the protective cover of spines has hardened

The young porcupine hardly needs its mother to protect it

Nor is the animal mother always alone in her efforts to protect her offspring. When a young dolphin is born there are several immediate dangers. First it must breathe, and this need is served by an instinct to swim upwards, break surface with its blowhole and take the first ration of air. The second danger arises from the newly born infant being still attached to the placenta, which is still within the maternal body, by the umbilical cord. The mother snaps the cord by making a quick turn in the water. She also watches the progress of the infant, and should it fail to rise to the surface she will put her snout under it to lift it, or she may raise it with her flipper. During these first few moments the mother dolphin must give her undivided attention to what her baby is doing. Once it has taken its first breath the tension is eased because the baby will thereafter rise to the surface regularly to breathe, and it is also able to swim as fast as its mother and instinctively keeps close to her side.

When the umbilical cord is snapped it bleeds, and blood in the sea quickly attracts sharks. So we find that when a dolphin is about to give birth another female will accompany her, ranging herself alongside the mother, shielding the other side of the baby and ready to help beat off sharks. This second female has been variously spoken of as a nurse, a midwife or merely 'aunty'. This means that we do not properly understand what her functions may be; indeed, it is not many years since this phenomenon was first observed in the seaquaria in Florida. We know now, from a few firsthand observations made in southern Africa, that elephants have a similar system. The mother-to-be has been seen to retire to a thicket, followed by another female, or maybe two, and then after a while the adult females emerge together with a baby elephant. What takes place inside has to be imagined because nobody would be so unwise as to venture too close—with 'aunty' on guard.

The greatest danger to a young dolphin or porpoise is in the first few moments after it has been born, when it must get to the surface to take its first breath. If it fails to do this on its own the mother may lift it up with her snout or her flipper

Right: a roe deer fawn, only five minutes old, takes an unsteady step towards mother

Below: looking particularly vulnerable but very alert, a young deer pauses for the camera

There is more certain information about hippopotamuses, but even this has only come to light within the last few years as the result of observations made by a Belgian zoologist in the Congo. They live in herds which each occupy a stretch of a river or large lake. The males and females do not mix indiscriminately in the herds. At the centre are the females and the young, usually grouped around a sandy bar on which they haul out to rest or to bask. The males are ranged around the periphery of this central territory, each male on his own, lording it over a part of the water and venturing into the central area only by the gracious permission of the females. Should his visit be unwelcome he will be driven out by several of the females. If a young hippo were to stray into one of the territories occupied by a male it would stand the chance of being attacked. Consequently, when the females go on land to pasture, as they must each day, there remains the problem of what shall be done about the youngsters. Long ago, before we thought of baby-sitters, the hippos had evolved such a system: the babies and the one- and two-year-olds are left in charge of an 'aunty'.

A few other animals that live in herds have similar nursery systems. Giraffes do something similar to the hippos, to mention one example, but in other species the care of the young is the concern of the whole herd. Yaks, living on the inhospitable uplands of Central Asia, are said to protect the calves from attack by the whole herd forming a circle around them. This form of defence reaches its highest development in the musk-ox of the arctic regions. Their natural

enemy is the wolf that preys mainly on the young. When one or more wolves approach the musk-oxen these form a phalanx with the youngsters inside and the adults in a circle around them, presenting their meat-hook horns to the enemy. From their ranks one of the males steps forth to do battle, and if he is defeated another comes forward to take his place. The musk-oxen use this form of defence not only against wolves but also against men, with the result that, in the past, when a young musk-ox was needed for a zoo it was found necessary to kill all the adults in a herd in order to get one baby.

Gorillas in Central Africa go about in troops made up of one old male, several females and their babies. If attacked the troop retreats, but the old male stands his ground, faces the enemy, and if necessary fights to the death. Then if the attack on them is continued it is the turn of the females to fight, even to the death. Indeed, almost the sole contribution made by the old male gorilla to the care of the young is to protect them, and the same is true for the males of such species as the European bison, the roe deer, and others.

The father hippo is not the only animal which harbours murderous intentions towards his offspring. One reason why the doe rabbit makes a special burrow for her litter away from the main warren is that the bucks have a tendency to kill the babies. This strange state of affairs obtains also in several mice, and we have the extraordinary situation in some of them that the male and female harmoniously occupy the same burrow until she is about to have her babies.

Then she drives the male away. Should he attempt to return she will fly at him again, biting him furiously. And if he is very persistent she will kill him. A recent writer has shown that bears have cannibalistic inclinations towards their young, and while we cannot always be sure that it is father killing his own offspring the chances are that this must often occur.

Baby seals suffer from the behaviour of the father, but for a different reason. At a certain time of the year, differing for different species of seal, the cows come ashore to have their pups. They are preceded by the bulls, each of which marks off a portion of the beach as his own territory, and within these territories the cows group themselves around the bulls in what are called harems. The young seals that are not yet in breeding condition occupy separate beaches, and the young bulls living on these 'bachelor' beaches not infrequently challenge the old bulls. An old bull so challenged rushes over to the boundary of his territory to engage the challenger. In his path he charges over cows and pups alike. This is the pattern for the sea elephant, as well as for other kinds of seals, and the male sea elephant may weigh two tons, which means that many pups are injured or killed by being 'steam-rollered' under the father.

One of the biological puzzles of recent times concerns the lions in the Kruger National Park in South Africa, and it has a surprising sequel. It was thought, some years ago, that there were more lions in the park than there should be, so some were killed off. Although the numbers were reduced, it was not very

Young elephants benefit from being in a herd and the young are watched over not only by the mother but by other females

long before there were as many lions as before. It looked as though the surviving lions had become aware of the thinning of their ranks and had produced more babies to make up the deficiency. Only within the last two to three years has the reason for this become apparent.

When a pride of lions makes a kill it is usually the lionesses that do the killing, but it is the lions that take the first pick. After this the lionesses take their share, and finally the youngsters. The first part eaten is the entrails. Since lions normally kill herbivores, the stomach and intestines contain partially digested vegetable matter, rich in vitamins. Where their numbers are thin a lioness may have to take care of the cubs entirely on her own. When in these circumstances she makes a kill she feeds the entrails to her cubs before eating anything herself. So we have a simple equation: when lions are numerous the cubs are starved of vitamins and their rate of survival is low, many dying as cubs, but when the numbers are thinned out all the cubs survive. This is the answer to the Kruger Park puzzle.

With some fathers attacking and killing their offspring, and with the example of the lions in mind, we can very well see that not all the dangers surrounding baby animals are from natural enemies. In all species many that are born fail to reach adult state. In some species the proportion is as low as one in two hundred or even more. These losses among infant animals we usually dismiss as being due to natural enemies, accident and disease. We are only just beginning

Lioness in Kenya, carrying her three-day-old cub in a typical cat-like fashion

to learn about animal diseases in the wild. We can guess, rather than know for certain, what the accidents are to which they are subject.

A pronghorn antelope kid reacts to danger by lying perfectly still

One cause of fatality is due to what is called imprinting. At a certain stage in the life of a baby animal it tends to follow any large moving object that comes within its field of vision. Normally this large moving object is its mother, and at this stage, when the young animal is impressionable, the image of the mother becomes imprinted on its memory and it continues to follow her around. The young chamois seems to reach the age of imprinting late, for a chamois kid nearly three months old has been seen to run towards a man. But this must be exceptional.

A caracal kitten prowls in the grass. When fully grown it will be well built for running and extremely agile

A roe deer fawn investigating the foliage. It has a tawny coat with three rows of white spots

Young bobcat

A warning difficult to take seriously for this cuddly lion cub

Pipaluk the popular polar bear cub born at the London Zoo persuading mother to retrieve his ball

Rhinoceros with young

Right: these prehistoric-look-ing American animals are known as armadillos because they bear a natural armour

Baby cottontail rabbits are born naked, blind and help-less in fur-lined nests

There was an occasion when a man riding his horse in Central Africa found the calf of a roan antelope coming up to his horse and nuzzling it between the legs. He tried to drive the calf away, but as often as he did this the calf returned. Then he saw the mother antelope approaching. A roan antelope has long horns and does not hesitate to use them. So the man found himself in a quandary. Unless he could persuade the calf to leave the mare there was the chance that the mother might attack. He quickly dismounted, pushed the calf well away, ran back to his horse and galloped off, and all was well.

It seems extremely likely, although we have no precise information on this point for animals in the wild, that there must be many baby animals which, at the imprinting age, follow a large moving object which happens to be one of its natural enemies. After that, it would be anyone's guess what the result might be.

growing up in the wild

The bulk of our knowledge of baby animals has been obtained from chance observations, and the majority of these are observations made of the young domesticated animals. To this can be added the study of animals in the laboratory. Consequently one sometimes wonders whether the picture we get in this way is a true picture. It is almost impossible to watch the actual birth of wild animals, or even the early days of infancy, either because these take place underground in a nest or in some other inaccessible place, or because the parent guards so jealously the secrets of her nursery. All too often, when an inquisitive naturalist has tried to obtain a closer look, the mother responds by killing and eating her babies. This is the result of a psychological upset which completely reverses the normal instincts of motherhood to protect and nurture her young to ensure their survival. Another obstacle to studying these intimate details is that so much time is required.

There is one outstanding instance in which the minute details of the lives of a single species of animal were documented in detail. The animal was the dusky-footed wood rat of North America. The two scientists who studied it took ten years to do so. And the results they obtained are set forth in a book of nearly 300,000 words. In one-hundredth this space a summary of what these painstaking scientists learned is attempted here, and even if we do no more in this chapter than learn a few of the day-to-day adventures of one kind

A particularly attractive baby rabbit, just three weeks old

This appealing wolf cub will grow into a powerful and intelligent animal

of baby animal it will be worth while if only to show how little we know about the others. Moreover, assuming that there must be some degree of similarity between the young of all species, it will enable us to fill in some of the details about other animals, if only by using our imagination.

It is not possible to show photographs of the wood rats doing all the things about to be described, but this is not necessary since most of their behaviour is illustrated by other animals throughout this book.

Wood rats are found over most of southern and western North America, as well as in some of the eastern states of the United States. They have very much the appearance of the more familiar black and brown rats which, originating in Central Asia, have spread or been carried to all parts of the world. The different kinds are coloured various shades of brown or buff, with pale underparts. Their special feature is that they build houses, variously called dens, huts or nests. Each house is constructed of sticks or other vegetation, with a roof, several entrances, sometimes on two levels or storeys, opening into passageways, and the passages themselves open into several rooms which serve as nests, food stores or middens.

A young bank vole eleven days old with the eyes beginning to open is able to walk only in a weak and uncertain manner, and is still very dependent on its parents

One of the first difficulties, a common obstacle to observing wild animals, is that the wood rats work mainly at night. Even when they move about by day they shun the light and keep to the shadows. On moonlit nights they are as likely as not to remain in the house and sleep, and if a torch was used on the dark nights when they were fully active this did little more than scare them. One of the first steps necessary was to have some means of identifying the individual rats. This was accomplished by live-trapping each in turn, marking it and releasing it, to see which house it went into, the houses then being marked with numbered labels stuck into the ground beside them. After that the only thing to do was to watch and listen, noting every detail no matter how small, in order to piece the story together. There were times when females caught in a trap would give birth before they could be released. From these it was learned how the mothers behaved towards their babies, and how the babies behaved towards the mothers in the early stages. When finally the family was restored to the house to which the female belonged, it was possible to see how the father behaved towards them and what happened to him.

Each female wood rat occupies a house separate from the male, and there she sleeps alone, coming out at night to forage. When out and about, a rat

Above: few animals can equal the squirrel in agility and gracefulness. Here a young red squirrel begins to explore

Left: a young cottontail cowers in the grass. Cottontails prefer to seek safety by hiding rather than running

Right: a very young golden mantle ground squirrel of North America just starting to learn to feed and on the threshold of being independent of its parents

meeting another stops at a short distance from it. The two point their noses at each other and sniff. Then they come closer until their noses meet. They lick each other's lips and each mouths the face and head of the other. So although the rats lead solitary lives there is still a fair degree of sociability. This may seem to have little to do with our subject, and yet it is important also in the lives of the baby rats, as we shall later see.

Social exchanges are not uncommon among animals, especially those that live in herds or in colonies. The behaviour of the wood rats recalls what was observed by another American scientist who spent four years studying nothing but prairie dogs. He found that they communicated with each other by touch, smell, by sight and by voice. The first is the more important because this is how individuals recognise each other, whether in ordinary group formations, in play or fighting, or in mating. The other senses play a greater or lesser part according to circumstances, but touch is probably the most important, especially in what has been called the identification kiss. This is exchanged whenever two individuals meet, each turning its head and opening its mouth to permit contact with the other. At times the kiss is prolonged, 'the animals maintain contact with their mouths and then one proceeds to groom the other...Male grooms female and vice versa; adults groom the young, the young groom

Right: a baby bushbaby: even the mother will easily fit into a man's pocket

An unusual gesture of friendship between a young fox and a dog

adults and each other. It is carried out by a rapid nibbling and pawing of the whole body, the teeth passing rapidly through the fur and touching the skin, the individual being groomed rolling over to facilitate the efforts of the one performing the operation.'

It is sometimes emphasised that there is little in the way of a courtship among mammals, certainly nothing comparable to the exaggerated courtship seen in most birds. The elaborate courtship is a means of forging a bond between the partners in a short while. Since to a lesser or greater degree some form of individual recognition is found in most mammals, either in the form of sniffing noses or some form of 'kissing', the need for an elaborate courtship is obviated, the social bond is being renewed constantly. Similar behaviour probably accounts also for the bond established between mother and young, and it may well be that the licking of the new-born infant has its roots in the same impulse.

So far as the wood rat is concerned, this seems to be borne out by the fact that the male mates with the female in the house nearest his own, and these are the two that will have met most frequently on their daily, or nightly, foraging. Having mated, the male takes up residence in the female's house and stays there until gestation begins, after which she grows intolerant of him and drives him out. As a rule he makes no resistance to her attacks, but departs, and thereafter he begins to wander about the area seeking a new mate. Should he resist her efforts to drive him out she may do him serious injury, biting him and lunging at him and returning again and again to the attack, inflicting wounds that, although not immediately dangerous, may suppurate and eventually prove fatal. It is tempting to see in this the origin of an irritability which, continuing after the young are born, may be expressed also against an enemy that approaches the litter, and which we construe as heroism when we see a female showing fight against a predator. It may even be this same irritability which, perverted as a result of shock, causes the animal mother to kill

94

The bond between mother and baby is to a large extent forged by the amount of licking bestowed on the baby in its early days and especially when the baby is newly born. Here is an eland cow licking its newborn baby

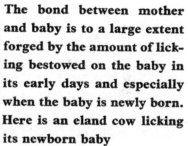

A mother also has to be patient with her young. Here a couple of playful tiger cubs romp over their mother

and eat her own babies, behaviour which seems to be most often seen in those species in which the driving away of the father is a marked feature of maternal behaviour.

This reduces heroism and other qualities to an everyday level, but, as the researches on the wood rats showed, a similar prosaic basis can be found for many of the apparently affectionate actions that take place between mother and young.

Not only does the female drive the male from the house in which she is going to have her litter, but she also vacates it when she is ready to have her next litter, or is ready for the next mating, leaving the youngsters in the house in which they were born. In this way she increases their chance of survival. They do not have to wander into the world at too early an age to seek a new site for a home, nor do they have to build at a time when their ability to do so is not fully developed. The action of the mother leaving the home must be regarded neither as forsaking her young, nor as a sacrifice that ensures them adequate shelter and protection. It is merely a part of the pattern for the species which ensures the maximum survival.

The young wood rats are born naked except for a few sparse hairs on the back. The skin of the upper parts of the body and head is grey, the ears are pink, as are the legs, tail, nose and the moustachial pads on the lips where the whiskers will later grow. The eyes are closed and within an hour of birth the babies begin to squeak and seek the underparts of the mother, where they eventually grasp the teats and hang on to them with their mouths. There is something to be said for the view that at this stage there is a parasitism on the part of the young and an automatic acceptance of the duties of host by the mother; her attachment to her young at this age is, at every step, the result of satisfying one instinct after another.

Sheltered by the massive bulk of her mother, Belinda a baby hippopotamus, makes her first public appearance

Hippopotamus mother and young

Young black bears playing

It's a long stretch for a young zebra to lick its tail

In the wood rat, at all events, the forging of a bond of affection seems to stem more from the initiative of the babies than the positive devotion of the mother. Such a harsh analysis is consistent with the mother leaving the young ones behind when she migrates to a new home; it is reinforced by what happens when the growing youngsters meet the mother again. Then it is the youngsters who try to mouth the mother's head or in other ways show that they have recognised her and that there is some bond between them. In all instances where this was observed, it seemed that the youngsters were taking the initiative and that the mother not only merely tolerated their advances but sought to break away from them in a short while.

This picture of the unrequited love of the young wood rat for its unresponsive mother is somewhat marred by the fact that all too often the youngster will conclude its display of affection by trying to push its head under her abdomen, which suggests that the memory of active suckling is the main factor prompting this behaviour. This should not be surprising since from the moment of

birth the search for nourishment has been the compelling drive of the young rat. Soon after birth, when the eyes and ears are still closed, the baby rat begins to squeal and to squirm towards the mother. Should she later happen to be away from the nest when the pangs of hunger set this sequence once again in motion the baby rat spends its time squealing, all the time lying on its back and pushing upwards with its feet. As soon as she returns, no less than when she is already present, this squirming on the back enables the baby to push its way under the mother's abdomen and seize one of the teats.

The strength of this hunger drive is such that once the baby has seized a teat it hangs on tenaciously, remaining attached most of the day even when it is not sucking. When this happens with rats whose behaviour is being studied in captivity it is not unusual to see the mother drag her baby unceremoniously across the floor of the cage. When freed and allowed to return to her house she may carry one of her two babies in her mouth and drag the other still attached to the teat. Similar behaviour was also seen in the wild under natural conditions, and although it is not possible to see into the houses it may be presumed that what was seen in the cage may well be commonplace in the home. The hold is so firm that when the mother has need to shed her burden she is compelled to 'treat her baby rough'. She mouths it on the back and shoulders, as if she were biting it, and once she has obtained a firm grip she pulls upwards until the young rat loses its hold. The whole operation is swift and business-like, and occupies no more than a few seconds.

When orphaned wood rats were being fed with milk from an eyedropper,

Above: the baby rhino stays with its mother for two years, and always walks behind her when going to pasture

The dark band across the face of the raccoon looks like a mask

Zebras with their foal between them, a formation which ensures protection for the young one

they took just as firm a grip on that also. The baby rat cannot be blamed for gluttony or unfilial conduct, for the incisor teeth are so constructed that they aid the infant's grip on the mother's teats. They may even make it difficult for the infant to let go. The teeth of the lower pair curve strongly outward to either side. The upper pair are also divergent but not so strongly curved, and their function is to press the teat into the crotch formed by the lower pair. The grip is also aided by the suction caused by the tongue working in the mouth.

This gripping action is not necessarily the result of hunger. On one occasion a young rat was seen to seize the base of the mother's tail and hang on just as tenaciously as it would have done to a teat, and while doing so it did not squeal.

This example illustrates well how the various instincts and actions dovetail into the pattern of the baby rat's life. With nothing in its mouth it squeals; grasping something in its mouth it ceases to squeal even although its hunger may be just as pressing and the object it has seized not nourishing. Therefore, while the infant squealing may sound pathetic to our ears, and while it may be a sign stimulus to the mother to return to her litter if she is out of the house, or to do something about it if she is in, this same squealing is no more than an instinctive response of the baby awake with nothing to occupy itself.

A mother tiger taking her three-month-old cubs for a walk

Above left: tigers, like so many other animals, educate their youngsters partly by love and partly by cuffing their ears; this cub looks a little shamefaced

Right: lion cubs nestle against their parents for both comfort and security

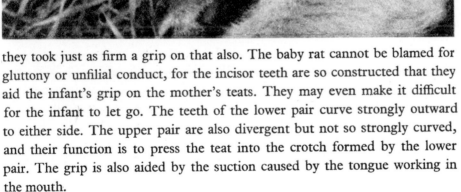

102

Above: a baby serval, a medium-sized cat of Africa, calling for its mother and listening anxiously for her response

Right: a baby caracal or African lynx

The instinctive response of the mother to the squealing and squirming of her litter is to crawl over them, so allowing them to grasp her teats. Sometimes the baby rats make clicking noises with their incisors. These seem to be a warning that the baby is searching for its mother, which is soon followed by the squealing, as the impulse to reach the mother becomes more urgent. This squealing, indicative of the search for a meal, is not so prolonged or high-pitched as the squeal that indicates pain or discomfort.

There is something impersonal, almost callous, about the way the mother wood rat picks up her baby to carry it. She puts both her front paws on it, one on the head and one on the thigh, and holds it pinned to the ground with its legs away from her. Then she mouths it, moving her mouth backwards and forwards and from side to side, giving every appearance that she is about to make a meal of the baby. And the whole of this manoeuvre is carried out as if the mother responded to no feeling in the baby and was merely impelled by an instinct to pick something up. In a later chapter we shall see that this is probably the whole truth, if the behaviour of the mouse opossum is a true guide to the attitude of the mother to its young.

Left: a dolphin calf must keep close to its mother to snatch each meal in a few seconds because there is no stopping for nursing, which is done as they swim along

Below left: very little is known about the habits of the giant panda in the wild, but a favourite food is certainly bamboo shoots

Above: young hair seal waits for the mother rather than following her about

Above right: polar bear cubs have a habit of wandering from the mother and becoming a little anxious until she finds them again

The reaction on the part of the baby is equally interesting. Theoretically, because it has nothing in its mouth it should squeal. This it does not do while it is being carried, thus revealing a valuable instinct, for if baby animals squealed when being transported from the old nest to a new one they would be likely to attract the attention of a predator. Clearly there is safety in silence when babies are being transported.

What is of even more interest is to imagine how this behaviour, the clinging of the baby wood rat to the mother's teat with such tenacity, and her crawling over her babies to present the teats to their mouths, explains the behaviour we have already discussed. It is only one step from this to the apparently purposive activity of the long-tailed field mouse, the deer mouse, the swamp rat and the various shrews which will be described later when we come to caravanning. Moreover, when the mother leaves the home followed by her offspring, which she does as soon as they are able to run about on their own, the youngsters follow in line behind her, as has been observed so often in the wild with other animals.

The question is sometimes asked when this subject arises, whether this habit of walking with such apparent obedience behind the mother is due to a fixed pattern of behaviour which is inherited, or whether it is taught. We have seen how it is largely taught in the young hippopotamus, and from time to time this or that animal in the wild has been seen to turn and chastise its offspring should it wander from this position. There was, however, positive evidence in this long and patient survey of the wood rat that when a young one strayed from this position behind the mother she turned and chastised it.

In spite of the extended period of time over which the two observers studied the wood rats, it may be that there were many small details which escaped their notice. But if we concentrate only on the behaviour they recorded, the impression we have is that the mother's attention to her offspring was limited to her instinct to carry them back to the nest when they strayed, to present her teats to them to suckle them, and occasionally to lick the foot or the flank of one of them. Apparently she did not lick them for cleaning purposes and it was observed that the wood rats from an early age cleaned themselves. One further contribution from the mother was to discipline her youngsters.

In a previous chapter the question was raised how far accident contributes to mortality among young animals. Here we have some evidence from which to judge, and this evidence suggests that chastisement is used for the youngsters' own safety. On one occasion, when a young male rat had been live-trapped for examination together with its mother, the youngster left the trap before its mother and crouched at the end of a log. When the mother later left the trap she rushed directly at him and hit him, causing him to fall three feet on to a pile of leaves. Whatever may have been her object, this rough treatment was received without a murmur and seemed to have the effect of making him follow her.

It was noticeable that there was a marked difference in the temperaments of different animals. Some were extremely nervous at being handled, others were quite placid. There is also a reflection of these differing temperaments in the way in which they build their houses. Some build neat nests, others slovenly nests.

There are ways also in which the young differ greatly from the adults. For example, a grown rat when alarmed moves its whiskers so rapidly that they are little more than a blur. A young rat when alarmed moves them slowly backwards and forwards as if the action of the muscles controlling them have not been fully co-ordinated. The young are also more careful in their movements, which suggests that other muscles have not become fully co-ordinated. A young rat is also more venturesome. For one thing, it will leap from a greater height than any adult. It is probably, more than anything else, the combination of venturesomeness from inexperience, with an inability to co-ordinate the muscles, which can lead to many kinds of accident that end in injury or actual fatality.

Young raccoons emerging from their nursery in a hollow log

A fawn of the white-tailed deer of North America makes no attempt to follow the mother until stronger on its legs than we see it here

Above: raccoons feed along the margins of rivers and these four young ones are dabbling in the water

Few of us are not moved by stories of the heroism often displayed by a mother in defence of her young. The more defenceless the mother is, the more we admire her courage. Inevitably we ask ourselves the question: why should an animal risk its own life for its babies? We can understand the human mother doing so, but we are surprised that animals, whose outlook on life must be so markedly different from ours, should also do so. If animals are so much actuated by instinct, these acts of heroism must be explainable in simple terms. Perhaps one of the most surprising events in the history of animal parents is the change that comes over the dog-fox when the vixen bears her cubs.

Foxes tend to be solitary animals, and the dog-fox is noted for his selfishness in the matter of food. The vixen may also be selfish, although this is difficult to judge, but certainly her mate will take all the food and pay no heed to her until she is about to have cubs. Then the father's greed turns to complete unselfishness. He brings food to the vixen instead of wolfing it himself, and, moreover, he will not touch a piece of it until she has fed. This unselfish attention continues as long as the cubs are with the vixen, and once the cubs are weaned the dog-fox helps the vixen to feed them. Then, as soon as the cubs are old enough to leave the parents, he goes back to his old selfish ways.

When we link such things with what we know of the parents, usually the mother but sometimes the father as well, transporting the babies, either as a daily habit or from one nest to another when danger threatens, we realise that it is the simple everyday events that forge a strong bond between parent and infant. The father fox probably loses his selfishness because of an inborn pattern called forth by a change in the vixen's scent.

All this seems natural and reasonable, but clearly there must be some way of accounting for it, especially when we come to consider the more surprising ways in which an adult of one species will adopt the young of another species. Acting on the general principle that the behaviour of animals is determined in large measure by sign stimuli, attempts have been made to reduce to precise rules why the adult animal is attracted to succour, protect or shelter the baby animal, always at inconvenience to itself and often at the risk of its own life.

Some years ago Lorenz put forward the theory that the parental instinct in human beings was called forth by sign stimuli provided by the human baby. It is difficult to test the theory by direct experimentation, but the arguments to support it are threefold. First there was the argument that dolls are so made that they give the three sign stimuli characteristic of a baby, which are a short face in relation to a large forehead, protruding cheeks and maladjusted limb movements. The second argument was that in the film industry the ideal

The adult polecat has a very sharp snout but the baby is snub-nosed and attractive; it is said the short muzzle is one of the things that makes baby animals attractive both to us and to natural foster-parents

Opposite page: a female cat that has just given birth to kittens fosters a young squirrel as if it were her own

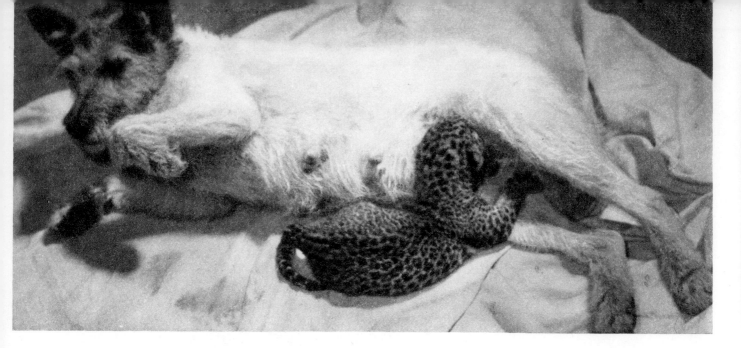

child actor was one that showed these characteristics to the full—except perhaps the maladjusted limb movements. The third argument was that childless women seek as substitutes those pets, such as Pekinese dogs and short-billed birds, which have short faces.

It is not unusual in zoos for baby leopards and other babies of the big cats to be fostered by bitches

Lorenz intended this to be no more than a theory, and he applied it strictly to human beings. As so often happens when an eminent man puts forward a theory, however tentative, this one was quickly picked up by the press in both hemispheres and for a while had a vogue. Moreover it was applied to animals, and in addition one point only was emphasised—the fore-shortened muzzle, which became almost accepted as the touchstone for evoking sympathy from man and beast alike. For example, one scientist was heard to explain the difference between our attitude to rabbits and rats on this basis. This was at the time when rabbits were being wiped out by myxomatosis, a horrible disease that revolted many people even although they recognised that the rabbit was a pest. The scientist pointed out that the people who were revolted by the effects of this disease were probably the same people who did not hesitate to put down what to him were revolting poisons for killing rats. He therefore offered the explanation that this was because the rabbit had a relatively short muzzle and the rat had a long sharp muzzle.

There can be little doubt that Lorenz's theory contained a germ of truth, but it was no more than a working hypothesis, and as such it constitutes an excellent debating point which can be best exploited by considering the arguments against it. There is no doubt that cinema audiences will murmur in approving chorus the moment the ideal baby, kitten or puppy appears on the screen, but the same people will be relatively unmoved at the sight, on the screen or in real life, of a baby hippopotamus. They may be interested, but not to the extent of falling in love with it. A new-born giraffe in a zoo will attract many visitors, although it has no sign of maladjusted limb movements and can move with agility almost from the moment of birth. With this the adult giraffe has a long muzzle, and the proportions of the face of a baby giraffe are almost the same at those of its mother. We enjoy the sight of young

Not only do animal mothers foster strange babies but strange companionships can also come about. Kittens and puppies playing together are no unusual sight

Right: this grown dog makes friends with a baby rhino

lambs skipping in the fields, and here again there is no sign of maladjusted limbs. A tame fox cub will draw murmurs of approbation, yet its muzzle is sharp, even if it is not so sharp as that of an adult fox.

If we limit this theory to the behaviour of human beings there are still difficulties. There must have been many occasions in the days before artificial lighting came into use when mothers had their babies at night; although they were unable to see them, there is no reason to suppose that they rejected them until daylight dawned and the short face and maladjusted limb movements became visible. And so far as animals are concerned there are many that always bear their young in total darkness. One has only to think of moles, rats, mice, badgers, and many others that give birth underground, where touch and hearing must be the operative senses. We have a partial key to this riddle in the behaviour of monkeys in zoos. There it has been found that most monkey mothers will accept their babies without question, but from time to time there is the mother who will have nothing to do with her infant until it cries.

Out of these conflicting arguments there emerges one fact: that for whatever reason mothers, whether animal or human, are readily attracted to young things. It is noticeable that when animals are kept in captivity they are apt to be disturbed at the sight of strangers (unless they are animals kept in zoos and are used to seeing strangers every day). These same captive animals will be less scared when the visitors are children than when the visitors are adults. Conversely, the person who will drive away a stray cat or dog from the door will almost invariably stoop with muttered sounds of affection to pick up a stray kitten or puppy. This characteristic is so strong that it leads to one of the more reprehensible aspects of pet-keeping. Every year hundreds of people adopt orphaned young animals rescued from the wild. They hand-feed them and rear them with care and devotion. Then as their pet grows to an adult they tire of it and try to find somebody who will give it a home. They have enjoyed its infancy and are quite prepared to ask someone else to take charge of it once that infancy has passed. They have been attracted to the young animal and lose interest in it once it is past the baby stage.

111

We are conditioned from an early age to all manner of young things, and by the time we reach maturity, the time when the parental instinct is fully ready to be evoked, we have learned to associate certain sign stimuli with infancy. To that extent the theory under discussion holds good, provided we recognise that of the components which make up the parental bond one of the m ore important comes from within us. When we apply this to animals, which do not have the same conditioning as we do, it is still something that comes from within that matters most. That something is the preparation of the body, including the senses and the emotions, by chemical changes such as the secretion of hormones, for parenthood.

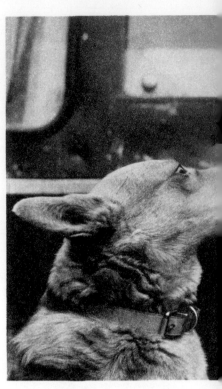

Gilbert White, the famous English naturalist, writing in the eighteenth century, told of a friend who 'had a little helpless leveret brought to him, which the servants fed with milk in a spoon, and about the same time his cat kittened and the young were despatched and buried. The hare was soon lost, and supposed to be gone the way of most fondlings, to be killed by some dog or cat. However, in about a fortnight, as the master was sitting in his garden in the dusk of the evening, he observed his cat, with tail erect, trotting towards him, and calling with little short inward notes of complacency, such as they use towards their kittens, and something gambolling after, which proved to be the leveret that the cat had supported with her milk, and continued to support with great affection. Thus was a graminivorous animal nurtured by a carnivorous and predaceous one!'

The same author gave another example of three baby squirrels taken from the nest and put under the care of a cat who had lately lost her kittens. The cat nursed and suckled the baby squirrels with the same affection and devotion that she would have lavished on her own offspring.

We can do worse than study White's further comments on these events: 'Why so cruel and sanguinary a beast as a cat... should be affected with any tenderness towards an animal which is its natural prey, is not so easy to determine. This strange affection probably was occasioned by that desiderium, those tender maternal feelings, which with the loss of her kittens had awakened in her breast; and by the complacency and ease she derived to herself from procuring the teats to be drawn, which were too much distended with milk, till, from habit, she became as much delighted with this fondling as if it had been her real offspring.'

Since Gilbert White's day there have been many instances reported in the press, of animals adopting strange 'fondlings', and many more by far have never been reported. For the most part they relate to she-cats and bitches. A typical example that I heard of through private sources was of a bitch which made a habit of going out into the fields and coming back carrying a young rabbit in her mouth, which she would try to nurse. In many other cases, the mother animal has lost her own babies, sometimes because they are likely to be a nuisance to the human owner of the mother. In yet other cases the adoption has been due to a false pregnancy, when the body of the female animal shows all the signs of approaching motherhood although there has been no mating. In a few instances, as with the bitch already mentioned, this strange adoption seems to become a habit, accountable for neither by loss of babies nor a false pregnancy. There are even instances in which a male animal will

A corgi shows unexpected affection for a black-faced lamb

do something very similar, although the adoption in such cases cannot be more than temporary. In all, however, we can point to a desiderium, as White called it, a conditioning of the body and the emotions to his form of behaviour. That the male animals should also sometimes show such symptoms is merely further proof that in all females there is something of the male, and that in all males there is not absent some of the characteristics of the female.

White's desiderium is merely an omnibus word for the internal changes, about which we now know so much more, that condition the body for parent-hood. And these examples of adoptions merely underline that all bodily pro-cesses can, on occasion, go slightly astray and lead to freak results, or at least to paradoxes. Not the least of the paradoxes is that a flesh-eater like a cat should on one occasion go out into the fields and deliberately adopt a leveret, yet the same cat will, at another time, kill a young hare as a matter of routine. This alone indicates that sign stimuli are not enough, and that the internal make-up of the prospective foster-parent is all important. It is the difference between the man who will take pleasure in seeing a young pig, or even rescue it should it be in difficulty, yet will relish the sight of roast sucking pig on the table.

A short while ago I received a letter from someone in Rhodesia which illustra-tes one of the paradoxes. The writer told how he was walking across the veld some years previously with a friend, accompanied by three dogs. Two were bitches and the third a very fierce cross-bred ridgeback dog. The dogs were out in front and were seen suddenly to concentrate at one spot, looking down and wagging their tails. They were looking at a very young duiker fawn—a duiker being a small antelope. The fawn had been cached there by its mother and it made no attempt to move. Surprisingly, the dogs made no attempt to harm the fawn.

The same writer then told how, two or three years later, he was out with his own four large dogs. A young duiker, not a baby or yet fully grown, walked out of the long grass about seventy to eighty yards away, and stood looking towards them. The dogs went off at top speed and those who were watching expected them to indulge in their usual chase. But the young duiker stood its ground, and the dogs, when they had reached it, walked round it, licked it and returned to their owner.

Even more remarkable was the third story, in the same letter, of how the writer was later walking through the thick bush with the same dogs when there was a scuffle not far away. The dogs ran towards the spot, and when my correspondent reached the spot he was surprised to find the dogs actually playing with a young duiker, patting it with their fore-paws, just as a puppy might play with another puppy. These dogs were full-grown hunting dogs that had tackled wild pigs, cheetahs, even lions.

There are very few anecdotes of this kind about wild animals showing tolerance, or even affection, towards a young animal which at other times would form their natural prey, but occasionally one does hear them. Millais, the well-known naturalist in Britain, records how he watched a fox playing for some time with a leveret, after which the fox went his way leaving the leveret unharmed. Even these few anecdotes suggest that this kind of event may happen more commonly in the wild than we are apt to suppose; probably just as on some occasions the internal condition of an adult animal may cause it to do something that conflicts with its natural predatory instincts, so there must be occasions when the behaviour of a young animal can divert the predatory instincts of hunting animals. Such ideas merely strengthen the notion that the bond between adult and young is the result of an internal conditioning of both parties together with sign stimuli. The combination of these is at its maximum when the two are natural parent and baby.

In recent years a number of experiments have been carried out with baby monkeys which shed light on the internal conditioning of infants. In experiments carried out by Harry and Margaret Harlow at the University of Wisconsin's Primate Laboratory the baby monkeys were taken from their mothers and provided with substitute mothers. One of the substitutes was in the form of a wire body with an artificial head and with bottles of milk in the appropriate position. In order to feed the baby had to climb on to the substitute body to reach the teat of a bottle. Other substitutes were constructed like this except that the artificial 'mother', instead of being a bare wire frame, was covered with terry cloth. It was found that given a free choice the baby chose the terry cloth-covered model. More important, the baby monkey, when offered two models, one of naked wire and the other covered with terry cloth, but with the bottles of milk fixed in the naked framework, would go to the wire frame to feed and then spend the rest of its time clinging to the cloth-covered 'mother.' It recognised the naked model as a source of food but needed to cling to the soft material for other bodily satisfaction.

The young of hoofed animals have somewhat different needs from those of babies born helpless and needing to be kept warm and sheltered. They are also different from those of the baby monkey who, with its parents clambering all the time through the trees, must cling firmly to the mother's or the father's body or fall to its death; its innate impulse to cling to a hairy body must be strong. Young hoofed animals, being more or less independent from birth, apart from the need for protection from enemies and the need to have a ready supply of food, do not have this same inborn impulse to cling and to cuddle close. One result of this is the ease with which young farm animals will take to foster-parents. A calf will readily suck from a mare or a foal from a cow. On farms where cows are kept and pigs are allowed free run, it is not uncommon for the piglets to find their way to a cow and feed freely from her. The mare or cow enjoys 'complacency and ease... from procuring the teats to be drawn.'

Here, then, are some of the guiding principles behind the formation of bonds between parent and young, especially with regard to foster-parents and their adoption of young of different species. This discussion can be appropriately ended with a story of recent date about piglets in South Africa. The sow with her piglets was kept in a sty, and one night a commotion was heard there. A wild bush pig had entered the sty, and in spite of the sow's efforts to protect her offspring the bush pig had eaten several of them. Since the domestic pig was derived from the wild pig of Europe, and since all wild pigs from whatever part of the world they may come are much alike, especially when very young, this should never have happened. These piglets, so readily devoured by the wild pig, bore all the sign stimuli which should theoretically have protected them from an adult pig, wild or domesticated.

A two-week-old spiny mouse being particular about personal cleanliness

A close-up reveals the traces of a recent meal round the whiskers of this wide-eyed lion cub

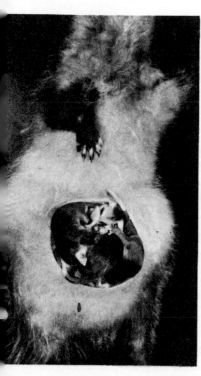

Pouch birth: underside of a Virginian opossum with eleven young in the pouch

A baby slow loris carried by its mother

The Virginian opossum is native to the south-eastern part of North America. It also lives in the northern parts of South America. Thus it must be a very familiar animal to many people, and it has been so for a long time. It looks something like a large rat, nearly two feet long, with a tail fifteen inches long. This is the animal that has given us the phrase 'playing 'possum', because when attacked it lies perfectly still and looks as if it were dead. When the animal attacking it has lost interest and wandered away the 'possum comes to life and makes its escape. At least, this is what is said, and it must be true because there are photographs of opossums doing exactly this. But latest reports suggest that this trick is not so common with American opossums as we have been led to believe.

This opossum, like those living in Australia, belongs to what are called the pouched animals or marsupials. The female opossum has a pouch, and when her babies are born they make their way into this pouch. There they stay until old enough to run about. Even then they often ride on the mother's back, and to give them more support she arches her tail over her back and the youngsters curl their tails round it.

At least, that is the story everybody had been believing for years until an American scientist looked into the matter a few years ago. He found that young opossums do not curl their tails round the mother's tail in the way everybody thought. How, then, did this story arise? In 1699, Maria Sibylla Merian went to Dutch Guiana in South America to paint butterflies. Having an empty corner in one of her pictures and no butterfly to paint in it, she drew a South American opossum with its young. In the years that followed other artists copied this picture and improved on it, and the naturalists believed the pictures they saw were accurate. Not only that, but they in their turn drew the Virginian opossum of North America in the act of doing the same thing.

Young opossums do cling to their mother's fur. For all we know to the contrary one of them may occasionally wrap its tail around the mother's quite by accident, although this has yet to be proved. But they do not strap-hang in the way everybody, including the scientists, have believed for so many years, and they certainly do not do it as a matter of habit.

No doubt one of the reasons why this story was so readily accepted as true is that, on the face of it, there would be nothing remarkable about it were it in fact true. Many animal mothers transport their babies in ways that are not much less remarkable, although the majority carry them in much the same way, by gripping them in their mouths by the scruff of the neck.

This is the way cats and dogs carry their babies, one at a time, transferring

them gently from one nest to another. Most rats, mice and squirrels also carry their babies in this way, although if they are forced to abandon a nest hurriedly and find another resting place for them they are not always particular about just how they pick them up. The mother may grab the baby by a leg or by the loose skin of the belly, but her grip is so gentle that she will not harm it no matter how she takes hold of it. It is like giving a dog an egg to carry: he will not break it no matter how long he carries it. Even my dog—a he-dog with a huge mouth and formidable teeth—has been known to carry a baby rabbit, so small that it was almost out of sight in his mouth, without harming it. Sometimes when one of these animal mothers is in a hurry to transport her baby she may even grip it by the head, and the mother bear habitually carries her babies in this way.

One of the most natural questions to ask is how the mother porcupine or hedgehog, with their prickly babies, manage to carry them. The answer gives us an interesting comparison. The young porcupine is able to walk almost from the moment it is born, so there is no need for the mother to carry it. It is, in fact, a precocious youngster, born with the eyes open and a dense coat of fur, and in the American porcupine, at least, the quills harden within a half-hour of birth. It is weaned at ten days of age.

The baby hedgehog is a very different case. It is born blind, a bloated bag of flesh, unable to walk and with its back covered with pimples. At birth the

Virginian opossum with her young ones riding pick-a-back after they have left the pouch

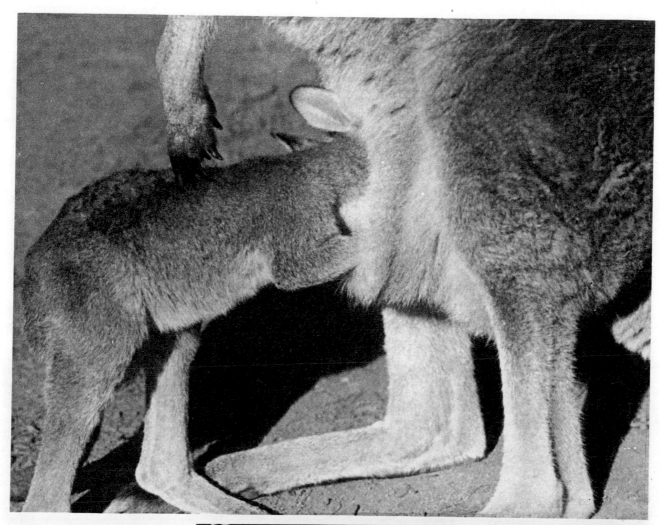

Even when it has reached this size, the joey still pokes its head into its mother's pouch to feed

A majestic family group of lioness and cubs

skin of the back is tight, the body swollen with water, but this is lost in two days. Then the skin sinks, and the spines, which were there before birth, protrude more and more, so that they appear to be growing rapidly. It is as well that they were cushioned in this way, to obviate injury to the mother during the birth process. The spines are first white, and only later do they harden and become dark. Moreover they are fewer in number than in the adult, so that the head, large in proportion to the body, and the nape of the neck, are naked, giving space for the mother to seize the skin in transporting the youngsters. After the spines have hardened, and before the baby hedgehogs are able to travel well on their own feet, the mother may carry them by the skin of the underparts.

Beavers have an exceptional method of transporting their young. The mother cradles her babe with her fore-legs, holding it against her chest and under her chin while she runs on her hind-legs. This is no more than we should expect from an animal which carries sticks with her forepaws, using them as hands. And it is not without interest to recall that a certain Major Roderfort in New York, towards the end of the eighteenth century, had a tame beaver

The young woodmouse of Europe about two days out of the nest

Mortality among lion cubs up to one year old is quite common; these two look particularly vulnerable

that had the run of the house, like a dog. This animal collected all the soft rags and materials it could find and made a nest for itself in the corner of a room. Then the household cat had kittens, and usurped the beaver's bed for the occasion. Thereafter, whenever the cat went out of doors the beaver took up a kitten between its forepaws 'and held it to his breast to warm it, and seemed to dote on it'. This lends colour to the assertion often made by writers on beavers that both father and mother are good parents and spend much time training and instructing the kittens—which in this sense are the beaver kittens. Whether they in fact train and instruct their young is, however, a little open to doubt.

However, it is wrong to dogmatise, especially about the private lives of animals. The fact that the young beavers stay with the parents for nearly two years means that they must learn a great deal from them, even if the parents do not deliberately instruct them.

It is among the animals which live in trees that we find the more unusual methods of transporting the young, and among these the method known as pick-a-back is in general use. The koala, also known as the Australian teddy bear—although koala seems a name much to be preferred—is a familiar sight in photographs for those living outside Australia. Monkeys and apes carry their young clinging to the body. Usually it is the mother who bears the burden, but the father also takes his turn.

The sloths of tropical America have long hook-like claws at the ends of their limbs, and with these they hang suspended, back down, from the branches for most of their time. The baby sloth clings to its mother as best it can, wrapping its legs around her body and using its claws like hooks to take hold of her fur, but its task is the easier because the mother, being upside-down, forms a sort of hammock for it. The sea otter that lives off the Pacific coasts of North America spends its time among the kelp beds floating on its back, and practically never comes ashore. Its front paws have toes so small that they are useless for grasping and its hind feet are large webbed paddles. The baby sea otter

has little need for toes to grasp its mother since it is able to rest on her body as she floats on her back, the youngster resting as comfortably as a child on an inflated rubber dinghy.

The sea otter is related to the river otter, but spends all its life in the sea. The single baby is relatively large at birth, with a well-grown coat and all its senses working, with strong teeth and able to swim from the moment of birth, and for a year the mother not only gives it constant attention, playing with it and grooming its fur, but also helps it find food when the suckling period is ended. Yet when the young sea otter leaves its parent it still has to learn the hard way how to get its own living, and not infrequently succumbs through lack of experience.

The flying lemur of south-east Asia does not fly in the true sense. It is the size of a domestic cat, with a sharp-pointed head and large eyes, and down each side of the body, from the chin to the tip of the tail, extends a membrane.

The koala of Australia—another pouched animal which carries her young ones pick-a-back when they are older

122

Above: the sloth habitually hangs upside-down and forms a convenient hammock for her young one

It lives among the trees, resting on the branches, and feeding on leaves and fruit which it collects by rapidly climbing among the branches. It can, however, move from tree to tree by long gliding leaps, as much as seventy yards for one leap. Living such an unusual life the flying lemur needs an unusual method of carrying its single baby, which clings to its fur while lying enclosed within the flying membrane as in a hammock.

Pangolins and anteaters suffer from some of the disadvantages of sloths. The great anteater of tropical America lives on the ground but has particularly long claws for tearing open termites' and ants' nests. The tamandua, another anteater of the same region, lives in trees and also has stout claws for ripping open ants' nests. Pangolins take the place of anteaters in Africa and Asia. They have bodies covered with overlapping scales. Some pangolins climb trees, others keep to the ground. All these animals have a single young at a birth, and this baby, a small replica of its mother, rides about on her back or clings

123

to the base of her powerful tail. The most remarkable of them is the African ground pangolin. Her single youngster clings to her tail, and if anything happens to menace its safety she brings her tail under her body, brings her neck under also, and in the chamber so formed shelters her baby, her body scales offering protection to them both.

The young sloth bear of India and Ceylon rides its mother's back like an expert jockey, maintaining its seat even when she is going at full speed. Baby baboons run it a close second in using this method of transport. Yet it is a matter of little importance whether the baby clings to the parent's back or to her underside, and all primates, whether monkeys, apes or lemurs, use one or the other method, varying the position or the manner of clinging but slightly. The Old World monkeys have a more prolonged nursing period than South American monkeys, and the mothers show greater solicitude for their babies. These not only cling to the mother by their own legs and arms but she uses one hand at least to hold her baby when moving with it through the trees.

These six-week-old opossums are normally carried on their mother's back but seem to have been temporarily deserted

124

This young giraffe, the tallest of all mammals, will grow to nearly 19 ft.

A proud and protective orang-utan mother gives her infant an affectionate cuddle

Young chimpanzee

The tigress carries her cub
gently but firmly by the scruff
of its neck, just as a domestic
cat does

South American monkeys differ somewhat among themselves. Newly born night monkeys are relatively helpless until about three weeks of age, whereas the capuchin baby clings to its mother's back practically from birth, with its arms around her neck and its legs straddling her waist. A young marmoset is carried at first by the mother, but after a short while the father takes it over, handling the youngster back to the mother at feeding time.

The lemurs of Madagascar are somewhat lower in the scale than monkeys. They range from the size of dormice to the size of a cat. All have well-developed tails and fox-like muzzles. Most of them are nocturnal and all feed mainly on fruit and insects. Except for the small mouse lemurs, which may have two or more at a birth, all lemurs have only one baby at a time, in which respect they agree with the monkeys and apes. Among the larger lemurs the newly born baby clings to the mother transversely across her belly, but for greater security throws its tail over her back and wraps the free end around its own neck. As with most other animals in which one baby at a birth is the rule, twins may sometimes be born. When this happens the two babies cling with hands in

Female three-toed sloth with her offspring nestles comfortably in the forked branch of a tree

129

Above: the red or lesser panda lives an arboreal life, sleeping in a hollow tree or in a fork between two branches

Left: a family of ring-tailed lemurs

Below: the extremely rare but very well known giant panda

opposite directions across the mother's abdomen, or else the father takes one of them, although he needs to hand it back to the mother to be fed, and then presumably he takes the other. This continues for some three weeks, after which the baby clings habitually to the mother's back except at feeding time.

One lemur, the squirrel-like aye-aye, the size of a domestic cat, sleeps by day in a large spherical nest in the trees, and there the babies are born and nursed. Several others of the lemurs also make this kind of nest.

Related to the lemurs are the slow loris, the bushbaby and the tarsier. The baby loris is carried clinging to the mother's long fur on her underside. The female bushbaby, so called because it cries at night with the sound of a human baby, prepares a nest in a hollow tree when about to give birth. Bushbaby twins are common, and after a period in the nest the baby bushbaby is taken out, carried by the mother in the same way as the baby loris is carried. Since the bushbaby mother carries her baby until it is well grown the burden of carrying two large twins is considerable.

The tarsier, which ranges from Sumatra to the Philippines, is the size of a rat, with a long tail tufted at the end and extraordinarily huge eyes. It is believed by some scientists to be very like the ancestral stock from which the human race sprang. The young tarsier is born in an advanced condition, fully furred and with eyes open, and able to scramble about on its own among the branches and twigs. It takes solid food at three weeks of age, this food including insects, lizards and small birds, but in spite of its precocity at birth the young tarsier does not disdain to be carried by its mother, and clings by its hands and feet across her abdomen. The local peoples, where the tarsier lives, maintain that the mother tarsier will carry her baby in her mouth, as cats, dogs and rats

Right: the mother bear carries her babies by holding them with the baby's head in her mouth

will do. On the face of it this seems unlikely, in view of the precocious youngster the mother tarsier has to deal with, but it is never safe to deny such stories without evidence. It may sound difficult to believe, but surely no more so than another trick to which the baby tarsier is said to be prone: when the mother is asleep the baby crawls over her and may even be seen sitting on top of her head. Women whose children are apt to wake them early in the morning by scrambling over them while they are abed may be less inclined, on reading this, to doubt the zoologists' assertion that the tarsier is closely related to the human stock.

It is very easy, as has been done here, to list the various animals that carry their babies pick-a-back, but it is less easy to give details of what takes place during the day-to-day living of these babies, for the simple reason that we have little information. Judging from a film taken of a slow loris and its baby which I have been able to study, riding pick-a-back may constitute more than merely being carried around. It may be part of the education of the baby.

When the slow loris moves through the branches and twigs it often has to squeeze through between two twigs. When this happens the baby climbs over the twig, letting go with its hands, reaching over the twig to grasp the fur of its mother as she moves forward below, then as her back moves forward beneath the twig the baby lets go with its feet, steps over the twig and takes hold once again of the mother's fur. Occasionally, the baby can be seen grasping a twig instead of reaching over it. The situation is one difficult to describe in words, except to say that although the baby is clinging to the mother it is also taking part in the business of clambering through the branches. It is easy to see from this that being carried around is not just a passive process. The baby is learning its way around its habitat. It is also being forced to make some effort itself and this gives it the first lessons in climbing. Moreover, as can be seen in the film, not only is the mother looking first this way, then that, but the baby seems to be copying her actions most of the time. This can hardly fail to be an education. Subconsciously the baby must be imbibing many lessons on what to do and what to avoid doing, where to look for food and what food to take, even perhaps what enemies to watch for and how to avoid them.

Although what is to follow next is not pick-a-back in the strict sense of the term it is next door to it, and for this form of transport we can start with the longtailed field-mouse of Europe, but what is said of this mouse also applies to the deer mouse of North America and several mice and rats of Africa. These all carry their young in their mouths at the earlier stages, but when the babies are able to run on their own they are transported clinging to the mother's 'apron-strings': that is, there is the instinct on the part of the babies, when alarmed, to take hold of the mother's nipples. There is also the instinct on the part of the mother to wait until her babies do this before seeking to escape. As a consequence we may see a mother field-mouse or deer mouse running away with her two babies holding on and running behind her, their feet moving in unison. No matter how uneven the ground, the mother and babies keep perfect time as they scuttle away like a diminutive locomotive engine pulling two trucks side by side.

The elephant shrews of Africa live among rocks over which they flee, when disturbed, leaping across the rocks to shelter in the crevices. The female bears one or two young, and these are suckled at teats which lie above her shoulder-blades. She carries her babies about holding on to these nipples, even when she is dashing over rocks or leaping into crevices. Moreover, when the mother is disturbed and ready to flee she makes sure that the young ones are securely holding on to her teats before she dashes away.

How much instinct enters into this kind of behaviour can be seen from what is known of the 'caravanning' carried on by certain European shrews, and also some shrews in South Africa and Asia. When the babies are young and first leave the nest they will at the slightest alarm, such as an unfamiliar noise, even a slight fall of rain, scuttle behind the mother. One of them then grips the fur near the root of her tail, another grips the fur of that one in the same way, and so on until the whole litter numbering eight or more is lined up in single file behind the mother, each grasping the one in front with its mouth. Then all move off, and as they do so they fall into step and they keep step all the time. Should the mother quicken her pace all the youngsters run faster to keep up. If she slows down, they slow down. When she leaps an obstacle the caravan goes over as one, in perfect timing and keeping in step throughout. It the mother senses immediate danger she stops dead still. Instantly the whole caravan does the same, freezing, without so much as a whisker twitching. When running swiftly caravans of shrews have sometimes been mistaken for snakes.

This caravan formation is usually in a single file, but two lines may be formed, or other patterns. But whatever the pattern may be, the babies grip so firmly that if the mother is lifted up she can be held with the whole litter depending from her in a string. What is even more remarkable is the way the whole family

Gripping her kitten by the scruff of its neck, a mother cat lifts her young from the nest. Many animal mothers transport their young in much the same way

132

Right: two night monkeys of South America with their baby riding on the mother's back

Below: common marmoset of South America carrying her young one

Right: this baby rhesus monkey is supported by its mother's left arm

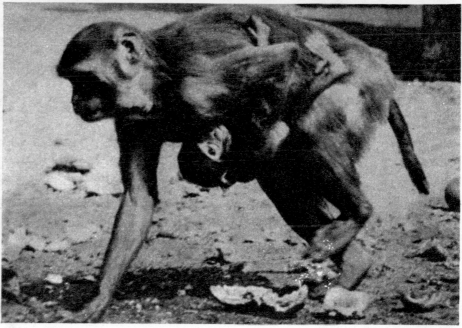

133

Right: the orang baby grasps its mother's fur, although she has her arm protectingly around it

acts with such unanimity. We may not be able to analyse why they do so, any more than we can analyse the means whereby the mother hedgehog manages to have her babies following her in orderly single file. The only thing we can say at present, and that is sufficient for our purpose, is that none of this depends on learning, or on the shrews or mice taking thought. We can only say it is the result of a pattern of behaviour that is inborn, and leave it at that.

Above left: the world looks upside-down to this baby baboon clinging to its mother Above: things look more normal to the baby as it rides on its mother's back

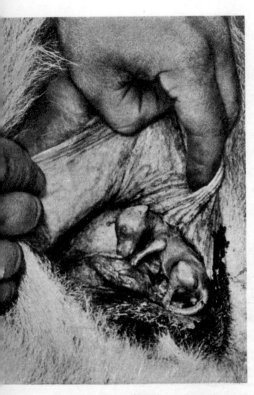

The baby kangaroo at birth is less than an inch long and only beginning to take shape; not until it is at least six weeks old does it begin to look like a normal kangaroo

It took nearly three centuries before the mystery was solved of how the baby kangaroo is born. The story starts in 1629 when the Dutch sea-captain, Pelsart, was wrecked on the Abrolhos Islands off the south-west of Australia. He saw the animal we now know as the dama wallaby, and to his astonishment he noticed that the female wallaby bore a pouch in front. He wrote of this: 'Their manner of generation or procreation is exceedingly strange and highly worth observing. Below the belly the female carries a pouch, into which you may put your hand; inside this pouch are her nipples, and we have found that the young ones grow up in this pouch with the nipples in their mouths. We have seen some young ones lying there, which were only the size of a bean, though at the same time perfectly proportioned, so that it seems certain that they grow there out of the nipples of the mammae, from which they draw their food, until they are grown up and are able to walk.'

It was the belief also of the Australian aborigines that the young kangaroo grew from the nipples of the mother, and this seemed to clinch the matter so far as western scientists were concerned. Admittedly Australia was a long way away, and scientists were few and far between in those days. What makes the story so astounding, however, is the way the truth of the matter was rejected for so long by scientists who came later and had more opportunity of learning the truth.

All but a few of the furred animals of Australia are what are called pouched animals, or marsupials, different in many striking ways from the animals we are used to seeing in other parts of the world. There are a few marsupials in New Guinea also, to the north of Australia, and then we need to go halfway round the world to South America, before we meet them again. The Australian marsupials include the kangaroos and wallabies, animals that are similar except in size, the opossums, phalangers, cuscuses, koalas, wombats and many others, such as the native cat, the thylacine or Tasmanian wolf, and the Tasmanian devil. In South America there are a number of much smaller marsupials, some only the size of a mouse, others like the woolly opossum the size of a squirrel, and the American opossum the size of a cat. The last of these is also found in parts of North America.

As far back as 1806 Professor Barton of Philadelphia described the birth of the young opossum: 'The young opossum, unformed and perfectly sightless as they are at this period, find their way to the teats by the power of an invariable, a determinate instinct, which may, surely, be considered as one of the most wonderful that is furnished to us by the science of natural history. It is not true, as has been often asserted, that the mother, with her paws, puts the young ones into the pouch.'

The young kangaroo, or joey, with its mother

Then in 1830, Alexander Collie, surgeon aboard one of H.M. sloops lying in Cockburn Sound, Western Australia, wrote: 'An officer of H.M.S. *Success* at present here, observed a kangaroo in the act of parturition. When the foetus was expelled—the mother was lying partly on one side—resting against the side of the cage where she was confined—and the very diminutive young, when brought forth, crept among the fur of the mother, towards her belly and towards the opening of the abdominal pouch: whilst she, with her head turned towards her tender offspring, seemed to watch its progress, which was about as expeditious as a snail. After it had made some advance, my informant, unconscious of the remarkable economy of generation in this class of Quadrupeds, removed the newly-born animal before it had reached its destination, which must have been the mouth of the Sac.'

Collie then observed the birth of a baby kangaroo himself and found that what his brother officer had told him was true. Yet neither his testimony nor that of Professor Barton in America found favour with the leading scientists of the day. To some extent this is understandable because ot two things: the behaviour of the mother kangaroo just before the birth and the small size of the baby kangaroo itself. The first of these suggests alternative explanations, and the latter makes it almost unbelievable that a baby so small and ill-formed could possibly travel unaided and settle itself in the pouch. The newly born baby of the largest kangaroo, which stands six feet or more high, is less than an inch long, and the newborn baby of the American opossum, which is the size of a fair-sized domestic cat, is only as big as a pea.

A film has now been made of the whole process of the birth of a baby kangaroo, from start to finish, so that we are no longer in doubt about what happens. But in the days before the film, or even a camera of any kind, people saw what the mother kangaroo did and drew their own conclusions—faulty conclusions as we now know. When the time is drawing near for the birth, the mother cleans the pouch in readiness. She holds it open with her fore-paws, grooms the fur inside, either with a paw or by putting her head into the pouch and licking, and generally pays a deal of attention to the pouch. She also licks the fur on her abdomen, from the opening of the birth-canal upwards to the mouth of the pouch. These are actions unlike those seen in any other animal, except for other marsupials. It seemed reasonable to suppose, therefore, that the mother either lifted the newborn baby up with her lips and placed it in the pouch or she lifted it up with her forepaws. What other explanation could there be for these elaborate movements made by the mother at about the time that the births was taking place?

Now we know that the baby kangaroo, as soon as it is born, makes its own way through the mother's fur, following the path she has licked into the pouch,

The white wallaby presented to the Queen, now in the Whipsnade Zoo, with its youngster peeping out of the pouch

138

and there seizes the nipple in its mouth and hangs on. At this stage it looks as little like a kangaroo as anything could. The eyes are closed, the ears are hardly discernible. The most conspicuous feature of the head is the disproportionally large mouth, wide open. Instead of the long hind-legs and small and very weak front legs of the adult kangaroo the baby has only the suggestion of hind-legs, and even these are crossed and hidden under the stump of a tail. And compared with these the front legs are strong and much larger. The only senses operating are those of touch and smell. The baby, if indeed it merits the name at this stage, makes its way through the fur with a sort of over-arm stroke of the front legs, guided perhaps by smell.

Perhaps the most interesting aspect of this birth is the clue it gives us to the workings of an instinct. The kangaroo at birth is only beginning to become an animal. Collie was right to refer to it as a foetus. The time that elapses from conception to birth in the case of the Virginian opossum is $12\frac{1}{2}$ days. Even in the largest of the kangaroos it is only 38 to 40 days. For the domestic cat, which is the same size as the Virginian opossum, the corresponding period is 55 to 63 days; and for a donkey or a deer of comparable size to the larger kangaroos the time would be a full year for the donkey, and 225 to 270 days for a red deer or a wapiti. It terms of these animals the kangaroo birth is very much a premature birth. This means that the brain can be only in the process of forming, and the nervous system can be at no more than a preliminary stage of development. Yet at least some instincts are already there. It sometimes happens, for example, that the baby making its way to the pouch loses its way or falls because it is dislodged. Experiments have even been carried out to test what happens then. Provided the baby can still grip the fur of the mother—that is so long as it has not fallen to the ground—it will re-orientate itself and find its way to its destination.

Once inside the pouch it still has to find a teat and take the teat into its

Even when fully formed and able to run about the joey continues to live in the pouch and returns to it after brief excursions into the world beyond

139

mouth. Should it be dislodged and fall into the bottom of the pouch it will still make its way back to a teat. In spite of its undeveloped state it still has the sense, if we may put it this way, to do those things that are essential for its own survival and future welfare, in spite of its premature condition.

From just under an inch at birth, the young kangaroo grows to about two and a half inches long at the age of six weeks. By that time the legs have changed markedly in their proportion. The hind-legs are now the longer. The tail also has grown from a mere stump to foreshadow the long strong tail of the adult. The ears are forming and the eyes are conspicuous, although they have not yet opened. The baby remains attached to the teat for nearly four months. During this time it has grown more and more to look like a kangaroo, and at the end of the four months has grown a coat of hair. After this it begins to take notice of what is going on outside the pouch. From time to time it will poke out its head or reach out and grasp leaves as the mother brushes past vegetation. Soon it begins to take excursions from the pouch, which is now capable of considerable distension.

The joey, as the young kangaroo is known when first able to leave the pouch, is at first no more than a foot high, and its hind-legs are then disproportionately long. It needs these because it is still dependent on the mother for shelter and must be able to leap back into the pouch when danger threatens, or when it is tired. At times, when the mother has to make a dash for safety, she may throw out this large infant. But she returns for it later. Meanwhile, the joey, safe in thick cover, instinctively freezes.

A question sometimes asked is what happens about the pouch sanitation. From the moment the foetus has entered the pouch and fixed itself to a nipple growth is rapid; feeding is thus rapid, and a by-product of growth and feeding is excrement. It may well happen, also, that as the mother moves about bits of leaf or twig may be brushed into the pouch, although against this we know that the opening of the pouch can be expanded and contracted, apparently under the control of the mother. Since the mother grooms the pouch before the birth it 's reasonable to suppose that she also keeps it clean by grooming

Right: young striped opossum seen after leaving the mother's pouch

A female kangaroo playing with her young one

while her baby is inside, although up to a short while ago nobody, so far as I could ascertain, had ever observed her doing this. It is reasonable to suppose that because the young one is so firmly attached to the teat the gentle pressure needed from the mother's tongue to clean the inside would not dislodge it. And later, when the joey has let go the teat, there would be no danger to it.

Carl G. Hartman of the United States has made a detailed study of birth in the Virginian opossum. The details are essentially the same as for the Australian kangaroo, but to these can be added the results of experiments Hartman carried out. He anaesthetised a female opossum at the moment that her babies were being born. Unlike the kangaroo, which has one young at a time, the Virginian opossum has several. He took some of these from the pouch and placed them near the opening to the birth-canal, the point from which they had made their journey to the pouch after being born.

One of them returned to the pouch at once. Two others took a short while to find their way back. The fourth lost its way and it was twenty minutes before it found its way back to the pouch. But the instinct and the necessary sensory equipment were there for the journey to be made, even if the fourth one faltered somewhat.

Although all the animals in Australia and South America that are related to the kangaroo and the opossum are called marsupials or pouch-bearers not all of them have a pouch. In some there are only flaps of skin, one on either side of the teats, that do duty for a pouch. In others, including the banded anteater, there is not even this. The mouse opossum also lacks a pouch, and one of these has been observed carrying her five young with her hindquarters held high to prevent them being rubbed on the ground. There is, however, no danger of their falling off. When one of them was held with forceps it was found possible to lift the whole family off the ground, in the same way as the family of caravanning shrews can be lifted.

There is a further similarity between the mouse opossum and the shrews and true mice that trail their young behind them. The female, like several other of the smaller marsupials, builds a nest of leaves and grass which she collects and carries either in her mouth or by wrapping her tail round a bundle of them. Whether it is that she needs to keep her mouth free for this purpose or not, she does not retrieve her babies with the mouth as one might have expected. The babies cling to her teats for the first part of their life. Later, when able to move about on their own, they crowd on to her back, and it sometimes happens that one may become dislodged and separated from its mother. She goes across to it and noses it under her abdomen so that it can seize a teat or grasp her hair. This apparently clever piece of behaviour reflects neither maternal solicitude nor intelligence, for the mouse opossum will do exactly the same for a baby mouse placed across her path—although, naturally, this unfortunate infant has no idea of taking hold of her.

What must be the finest piece of maternal juggling has been seen in the mouse opossum. A female returned one of her dislodged babies to its place on her back by putting her snout under it as it lay on the ground, tossing it into the air and catching it neatly on her back.

The koala, probably the best known of all animals that carry their youngsters on the back, would be unable to duplicate this trick for the simple reason that were its baby to lose its grip on her it would take a tumble to the ground from the upper branches, where koalas habitually live. This may be why the habit of riding pick-a-back is developed in this species to so exaggerated a degree. It may also be the reason why the koala has only one young at a birth. The newborn koala is small enough, only an inch long, whereas the mother is a stocky two feet high, so it has the pouch all to itself, as in the large kangaroos. There it remains for six months, by which time it is fully furred and able to climb out. Climbing on to the mother's back it takes up the position it will continue to occupy until it is a year old, and nearly as big as the mother herself.

As if this were not burden enough, it sometimes happens that one mother will take charge of the growing infant belonging to another koala. The reason for this is not clear, but it is known that when several females carrying their babies happen to congregate at feeding time the youngsters may get mixed up, several of the mothers finding themselves with the wrong baby to feed. Contrary to the usual state of affairs in the animal kingdom, the koala mother makes no protest at having to suckle a baby not her own. Then, when feeding is done, the babies sort themselves out, each returning to its rightful parent.

Again and again, as one studies the workings of instincts and the way animals are helped to survive by their natural endowment, everything seems to fit so beautifully together. Then come the discordant notes. And nowhere is this more obvious than in considering the number of teats female animals have compared with the number of babies they have to feed. Rats have five pairs of teats, but wehreas the average litter for the brown rat is eight a female may have as many as twenty young at a birth. This is not so serious as it sounds because large litters occur when there is abundant food for the mother, which means that her supply of milk will be copious and the youngsters can take turns at feeding.

In marsupials, where the babies are permanently fixed to the teats for the first part of their life in the pouch, there is no such compensation for any discrepancy. In most marsupials the number of babies occupying a pouch is less than the number of teats available. The brushtailed opossum, the commonest of the Australian opossums, has two teats and there is rarely more than one young in the pouch at a time. By contrast the native cat, another well-known Australian marsupial, has only six teats and she delivers anything up to twenty-four babies at a birth, the surplus being doomed to death from the start. This singularly bad arrangement is the more striking when we find that some of the bandicoots have no more than two to four young at a birth, with eight teats to feed them.

The eight-inch-long baby of a short-tailed wallaby in the London Zoo leaps from the mother's pouch; the keepers were unaware of its existence until a short while before this picture was taken

oddities and ends

In this book we have used the word 'animal' in its popular sense, meaning mammals, whereas in fact 'animal' includes all living things with the power of movement, from elephants to earwigs and microscopic forms. But there would not have been room for them all in one book.

The marsupials or pouch-bearers are animals (that is, mammals) which carry in their anatomy many features that are reptilian in kind, and it is believed they represent a stock that branched early from the reptiles of long ago. It is also believed that so many different kinds are found in Australia, as compared with South America, because the continent of Australia became isolated early in recent geological times. There is another kind of mammal in Australia that also owes its survival to this isolation. This is the egg-laying mammal, which is isolated in another sense also. The two egg-laying mammals are the echidna or spiny anteater and the platypus or duckbill. They are isolated in the scientific sense not only by their peculiar structure, and the fact that they lay eggs instead of giving birth to live young, but also because so far no fossils have been found that would shed light on their past history.

The first of these egg-laying mammals, the echidna or spiny anteater, includes two species, one of which ranges from New Guinea in the north, through eastern Australia to Tasmania. The second is found only in north-west New Guinea. The best-known of the two, the Australian, has a rounded body up to sixteen inches long, and its upper parts are clothed with a mixture of spines and hair. It has powerful claws used for digging out termites and other soft-bodied insects, and a long beak-like muzzle with a long tongue for picking up the insects. It is without teeth and crushes the insects with horny serrations on the back of the tongue, which works against hard ridges on the palate. Altogether it is peculiar, as is its manner of reproduction, and too little is known about that to merit more than a few words about it.

The female lays one egg a year. This has a soft parchment-like shell, and as soon as it is laid the female pushes in with her muzzle into a pouch on her abdomen. In a few days it hatches and the young echidna is nourished with milk that oozes from two slits on the mother's abdomen. It is carried in the pouch until its spines begin to grow, after which the mother places it in a shady spot to continue growing on its own, and from there it must make its own way into the world. As soon as the youngster leaves the pouch this disappears until the next breeding season. It is only a temporary structure.

The duckbill breeds once a year also, but the story of its early life is as complicated as that of the echidna is simple. The adult duckbill is nearly two feet long, its body rounded and barrel-shaped, and it has a flattened six-inch

The wombat is badger-like, running on all fours, but it also bears its young in a pouch in the same way as a kangaroo, the youngster leaving the pouch only when it is well grown

Young chimpanzees master simple skills quickly and show some ability to reason. They often learn and develop faster than young humans

tail. Its legs are short, strongly clawed and webbed, since the duckbill spends most of its time in water. Its muzzle is beak-like, sensitive, purple-black on the upper surface, mottled yellow and black underneath. Its coat is made up of long crisp curly hairs with a dark underfur.

The female lays two eggs once a year, and in preparation for this she digs an elaborate tunnel which may be from twenty-four to one hundred feet long, but never more than a foot below the surface. The tunnel is tortuous and leads finally to a nesting chamber, and at intervals throughout its length it is blocked by the female making barriers of soft earth, six to eight inches thick, tamped into position with her tail. Before constructing these partitions she carries nesting materials, grass and leaves, into the end chamber, wrapping her tail round them to transport them. The two eggs are laid fifteen days after mating. They are soft-shelled, a dirty yellowish-white, and only three-quarters of an inch in diameter. But she does not just lay the eggs and leave them. The female holds the eggs on her abdomen until they hatch nine or ten days later, when the newly born babies feed on milk secreted from slits on the mother's abdomen.

The young duckbills are born blind, naked and helpless, and develop very slowly. Their eyes open at the age of eleven weeks. By the time they are two months old they are covered with a fine fur. They are not weaned until they are fifteen weeks and do not take to the water until they are four months old.

The mother duckbill has no pouch, so that the babies must cling to her, although she curls her tail around to assist them in this, and there is a striking similarity between the newly hatched duckbill and the baby kangaroo, despite the fact that the former is relatively much larger. When first hatched the duckbill is just under three-quarters of an inch long, a bean-shaped mass with the head only just discernible, a very short beak, a stump of a tail and very short legs. When four days old the length has increased by a half, by the seventh day it has grown to nearly four times the first length and is beginning to show more resemblance to an animal, rather than a shapeless mass of flesh. By the fourteenth day it is nearly four inches long, the duck-like bill is becoming pronounced, and the legs and feet flattened and more like the webbed feet of the adult. At six weeks of age the young platypus measures about

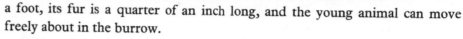

The Mongolian Wild Horse, or Przewalski's Horse, is very rare in the wild. However, captives in zoos throughout the world are breeding successfully

a foot, its fur is a quarter of an inch long, and the young animal can move freely about in the burrow.

At the other end of the scale from the primitive echidna and platypus are the bats, which have taken on such a specialised life. Nevertheless, there are similar peculiarities and problems about the birth of the young. Bats are the only mammals capable of true flight, and for this their fore-limbs have become modified to wings. Had bats developed from the marsupial stock there would have been advantages in being able to carry their young in a pouch. As it is, the nearest to flying animals among the marsupials are the flying phalangers, and these merely glide from tree to tree, using a fold of skin stretching from the front legs to the hind-legs on each side as a parachute. The baby phalangers are carried in a pouch from soon after birth, as is common among the marsupials, and later, when able to leave the pouch and before becoming independent, they ride on the mother's back as she glides through the air.

Because of their unusual way of life bats cannot afford to have large families. The rule is one young at a birth, but sometimes there are twins, and some of the migratory bats of North America have as many as four babies at a time. Baby bats are born blind and naked, and although small they are well formed and their wings are well developed. In some species, as in the long-eared bat of Europe, the mother forms a sort of pouch into which the baby can be born, by hanging horizontally, clinging with the hind feet in the usual way and also taking hold with her thumbs, which are free of the wing membrane and normally used for climbing around. With the wings half raised, and with the interfemoral membrane—the membrane that extends from the hind-legs to the tail — a convenient hammock is formed.

With most bats the expectant mother hangs head downwards, as in the normal sleeping or resting position, and although she may give some help to the newly born with her wings, to a large extent its life hangs by a thread—that thread being the umbilical cord. The baby is born and drops to the level of the mother's mouth, held by the umbilical cord still attached to the placenta. In due course the placenta comes away and is, as usual, eaten by the mother, and in doing this she severs the umbilical cord. During the early stages of birth, while the baby bat hangs suspended by its cord, the mother licks it to clean off the birth fluids. If all goes well the young bat will have progressed far enough to be able to cling to its mother before the placenta is extruded and the umbilical cord severed. Should it so happen, however, that the baby has not taken hold by the time the cord is cut, it falls headlong to its death.

Our knowledge about the birth and upbringing of bats is only just beginning to accumulate, and there are many questions still remaining to be answered. One of them is about the percentage of young bats that come to an untimely end in this way. For that matter we know little about why young bats do fall to the ground, except the general assumption that accidents will always happen in the best regulated families. Certainly, it is not unusual to find baby bats on the floor below the roost, and not all these are newly born. Sometimes the mother bat will retrieve her lost baby, although here again we are still in need of more information. Even so there are many stories, some of them well authenticated, of a baby bat lying on the ground, of the mother swooping down, landing on top of it, mantling it with her wings and then flying off, leaving only the bare ground beneath her as she takes off to show that she has borne her lost baby away with her.

Even more remarkable are the stories of how somebody has found a baby bat lying on the ground, has carried it away to hand-rear it, has later passed the same spot carrying the baby bat in his hand, and has had the mother bat circle him, refuse to leave him, and land on him in an effort to be reunited with the baby. Presumably the mother hears the ultrasonic squeaks of distress of her lost one, which are inaudible to our ears, and has recognised the voice as that of her own offspring.

The baby bat opens its eyes for the first time at five to nine days old. Prior to that, with only scanty hair on its body and pale-coloured wings, it has clung to her with hands and feet as well as its mouth, and has been carried about by her not only when she is in the roost but also when she goes out hunting. So from the first the young bat gains flying experience, if only the feeling of being airborne. This is a remarkable feat for the mother, since the average baby bat weighs about a third the weight of the mother, and it is not many weeks before it is half her weight. At the end of a fortnight or so the mother can no longer sustain this burden, and she then leaves her growing baby behind when she goes hunting. She parks it in the roost, leaving it hanging in company with the other babies, all of whom have been born at virtually the same time. All this is made the easier by the fact that during the nursery period male and female bats occupy separate roosts, so there are no clumsy males to dislodge the youngsters waiting for the mothers' return. Those roosts with females and babies only are appropriately called nursery roosts.

When we say the young bat hangs on to the mother by hands, feet and mouth, it means that the baby grasps her fur with the toes of the feet, grips with the thumb that lies free of the wing membrane, and holds on to her nipple with its mouth. The number of teats varies from one kind of animal to another. In many they form two rows down both the chest and the abdomen. In others, like the hoofed animals, they are reduced to two pairs in the groin. With some animals, notably the elephant, the teats are reduced to one pair lying on the chest, and in the sea cow they lie in the armpits. The insectivorous bats, known

The lesser horseshoe bat carrying its young one. The mother has been banded and carries an identification ring on the right wing

The young koala makes its first appearance from the pouch after about six months. It is then carried on mother's back until it is half grown

as the vespertilionid bats, to which the majority of small bats belong, have a single pair of teats on the chest. These not only supply the baby with milk but also serve as supports by which it can cling with the mouth. In the horseshoe bats there is a second pair, known as false teats, in the groin. These do not supply milk but are used by the baby for hanging on to the mother.

In about six weeks after birth the young bats are able to take wing and look after themselves. It is then that there is a considerable reshuffling. The nursery roosts are abandoned, and males and females, as well as the young of the year, assemble during the day in mixed roosts.

In passing, mention may be made of the nursing habits of the sea cows already referred to. These, the manatees living in tropical waters of the Atlantic, on both African and American coasts, and also the dugong, ranging across the Indian Ocean and south to the northern coast of Australia, are reputed to be the original mermaids of the legend, because they are said to hold their young to the breast. Their babies are born singly or in twos under water, as with the whales, and like the young whales, porpoises and dolphins must

quickly come to the surface for the first breath. Unlike the young whale the baby sea cow needs to be brought to the surface by its mother for its first gulp of air. This she does by lifting it either on her back or her shoulder. This first visit may be prolonged, and in one instance the baby was held up out of the water for as much as three-quarters of an hour. Thereafter, the youngster is brought to the surface every three of four minutes throughout the twenty-four hours of each day, but the interval between visits to the surface is gradually increased. Even so, this would represent an enormous labour for the mother were she left alone to tend her babe, but the father is devoted to his mate and offspring and takes turns in holding it and attending to it.

The baby manatee or dugong is born a year after the parents have mated, and it is not weaned until it is eighteen mounths old. Sea cows are related to elephants, and the young elephant has an even longer period of parental care. Born twenty-one months after the parents have mated the single calf stands three feet at the shoulder, weighs about 200 lb., to the sea cow baby's 40 to 60 lb., and is covered with coarse black hair. As in the sea cow, the elephant's teats are pectoral (on the chest) and the young elephant sucks with the mouth, continuing to be dependent on the mother for nourishment until it is two years old, and it remains with her for another two years after that.

The elephant holds the record for duration of parental care. The gestation period is up to 670 days, while the great Indian rhinoceros and the hippopotamus, the next two largest land animals, have gestation periods of 510 to 548

Above: young aardvark, an animal about whose habits little is known; it feeds on termites and full grown is the size of a pig, with its body sparsely covered with long hair; the youngster has much shorter hair more evenly spread over the body

Above: a red fox cub resting

Below: an eight-week-old brown bear cub

and 210 to 255 days respectively. The blue whale, the largest animal of all time, has a much shorter gestation period than the elephant—under the year—but holds the record for size of baby. A fully grown blue whale may be anything up to 100 feet long, and the newborn blue whale is about 24 feet long and may weigh 4 tons.

In the reverse direction, we can turn to a groung squirrel for brevity of infancy, and especially to that race of ground squirrel which lives on the barren tundra of Point Barrow in Alaska. There the snow persists for most of the year and the ground is permanently frozen to a depth of many hundred feet. With the short summer the earth may thaw to a depth of a few inches, at most a few feet, the maximum thaw being in areas of good drainage where the soil is sandy and raised in hillocks. It is on these islands of land, where the risk of flooding in spring is low, that the Barrow ground squirrels have their burrows.

These squirrels sleep for nine months of the year and must cram into the remaining three months all the activities that make up life. They leave their burrows in May, while the ground is still covered with snow and the dry and dead vegetation of the previous year is still hidden under the mantle of white. During the first days they do not venture far from their burrows, and feed on the stores accumulated in them during the previous short summer season. As the air warms the snow recedes and the vegetation springs to life. This, for the ground squirrels, is the beginning of a new season. There follows a period of intense activity, with the squirrels running from burrow to burrow and a good deal of fighting, and all this continues until the season closes down on them again and they go once more into hibernation.

Over and above this general activity mating takes place towards the end of May. The young are born twenty-five days later in litters of five to ten, naked and blind, their eyes opening twenty days later. Meanwhile, the babies start to grow hair on the second day, and by the tenth day the body is covered all over with short fur. Twenty-two days after being born, and only two days after the eyes have opened the young ground squirrels leave the burrow and start foraging. At first they stay close to the burrow, but gradually go farther afield. Perhaps by the end of a fortnight some of them may have gone as much as two miles from the parental burrow, there to dig a fresh burrow or to occupy one that is vacant.

With her family gone the female starts to feed as much as possible, to repair the loss from feeding and brooding her young. The males are polygamous. They wander about in search of females, and they also start to feed heavily. By the end of August or the beginning of September all the adult squirrels have laid in a store of fat in their bodies. They have repaired and cleaned their burrows, and are ready for hibernation, having accumulated fresh nesting material and laid in another store of food. Throughout they behave as if aware of the urgency of the situation. They make the greatest possible use of every moment. Neither rain, low temperatures nor bitter winds deter them. They return from feeding on the scanty vegetation with their cheek-pouches stuffed with food and a bunch of grass held between the teeth for the new nest. Not a moment must be lost and no unnecessary journeys made. They feed on anything: leaves, stems, flowers, roots, seeds, anything vegetable—or animal for that matter, including carrion and offal, or the carcasses of any of their mates that have died. Yet for all this seeming urgency they still take time off. The sun is above the horizon in these latitudes for twenty-four hours of the day, from the second week in May to the first week in August. Yet the ground squirrels keep to a working day of seventeen hours or so, and then only at the peak period of activity. Presumably they need some rest each day after working so hard.

The speed at which they work can be judged by the following measurements: a squirrel has been known to excavate a burrow thirty-seven and a half feet long inside twenty-four hours, and the longest burrow seen measured nearly seventy feet. The maximum depth of a burrow is eight feet. Since the squirrels are not specially equipped for burrowing, their legs and claws not being particularly strong—certainly no more so than most squirrels and probably not so much so as in most of their kind—these feats are remarkable. They are an

Kinkajous can swing from the branches of trees with their tails, but the ability to grip with its tail does not come to the baby kinkajou until it is about a month old

Cottontail rabbits do not excavate burrows and prefer to hide in thickets rather than run from danger. Here a young cottontail relaxes in grass

indication of the explosive expenditure of energy during this brief season above ground.

If the achievements and activity of the adults is remarkable, those of the young are even more so. Born in early June, they achieve the same weight as the adults in about forty-two days. Following that they have to find or dig a burrow, construct a nest, provision the burrow with food, and make all preparations for the winter sleep, which they commence a month later than their parents, in late September or early October.

Barrow ground squirrels have practically no enemies, yet their populations remains more or less static in spite of the litters of five to ten. There are several probable causes of this. First, the female will eat any young she cannot adequately brood. This is a hard region and a hard life, and even infanticide must be accepted. There must also be a heavy mortality among the young. Many of them are no doubt forced far afield to find new living space, on to ground between the 'islands' with even more scanty vegetation and less chance for them of survival. Even without these hazards there is keen competition for the available supply of food, with the dice loaded against the youngsters, who through their lack of experience may fail to find enough food during the active period, fail to store enough in their burrows, or fail to burrow sufficiently deep so that they may become frozen in their burrows should the weather prove abnormally severe during the period of hibernation.

It seems also that cannibalism may occur, the first to awake eating those that are still asleep. Cramming a year of life into three months must bring greater hazards for the young. And there is no time for prolonged parental devotion!

acknowledgments

A. W. Ambler 133

Toni Angermayer 99, 137

Barnaby's Picture Library 4, 16 T, 80 B, 101 TR, 130/1

Barratt's Photo Press 77 T

Des Bartlett, Armand Denis Productions 64, 69 T, 72, 84 B, 94 T, 95 T, 103 TL, 103 TR, 148

Bavaria-Verlag 134 L

Kay Breeden 139

British Museum 116

Mary Browning 62

Jane Burton 12 L, 14, 21, 22, 23 T, 23 B, 24, 25 T, 28/9 C, 37, 39, 48, 51, 79, 90 T, 108, 111 L, 115, 144/5

Camera Press 63 R, 129

Bob Campbell, Armand Denis Productions 134 R

John Carnemolla 119 T, 147 TR

Ken Denham 127

Fox Photos 9, 17, 87 T, 102 TR, 131 R, 133 TR, 138, 142

Freelance Photographers Guild 57, 61, 66, 68 TL, 68 TR, 86, 98, 107 TL

Granada TV 145

C. A. W. Guggisberg 42 T, 42 C, 42 B, 43, 49, 82, 83, 103 B

Ingmar Holmåson 85

Peter Keetman 15

Keystone Press Agency 18, 30, 41, 68 B, 70 R, 70 L, 71, 87 B, 89 T, 109, 119 B, 128, 149 B

Russ Kinne 26/7

Geoffrey Kinns 50 T, 58

Frank W. Lane 45, 80 T, 104 T, 117, 118, 122, 123, 151 B

Leonard Lee Rue III 81, 89 BL, 92 T, 92 B, 124, 149 B, 151 TR

John Markham 46, 47, 50 B, 91

Mirrorpic 111 R

Rex Moreton 35

The Mustograph Agency 21 B, 60 B

National Parks Board of South Africa 55

Okapia-Grzimek Frankfurt 76, 110

PAF International 63 L, 65

P. A. Reuter 96

Ed Park 74, 84 T, 90 B, 107 TR

Neave Parker 60 T, 94 B

D. M. Paterson 54 T, 121

Pictorial Press 2, 13

Axel Poignant 136, 144 L

Paul Popper 100

Réalités 105 R

Rex Features 12 R, 20, 33, 38 T, 38 B, 54/5, 59, 112/3, 132

T. W. Roth 34 L, 96

H. W. Silvester 56

W. Suschitzky 5, 10, 11, 16 B, 19, 20 L, 25 B, 26 T, 28, 29, 31 T, 31 B, 32 L, 32 R, 34 B, 40, 44, 67, 78, 97, 102 TL, 126, 130 TL, 130 B, 133 B, 135, 140, Endpapers

Syndication International 7 B, 52, 69 B

Tate Gallery 8

Ronald D. Thompson 147 L

Sally Anne Thompson 36, 125

Simon Trevor, Armand Denis Productions 53, 75, 88, 101

John Warham 141

World Wildlife Fund 104 B

Joe Van Wormer 73, 77 B, 93, 105 L, 107 B, 114